HELP® for Langua

MW00609585

by Andrea M. Lazzari

Skill	Ages	Grades
■ language	■ 8 through adult	■ 3 and up

Evidence-Based Practice

■ Students are expected to make inferences in authentic reading situations as well as on high-stakes standardized tests (McMackin & Newton, 2001).

■ Standardized tests require students to predict, draw conclusions, elaborate, explain, and make analogies (McMackin & Newton, 2001).

■ Grammar, discourse structure, and metalinguistics are all connected to reading and writing achievement and required for text comprehension (ASHA, 2001).

■ Summarization is a skill that helps students identify main ideas and recall information needed to answer comprehension questions (NRP, 2000).

■ Answering wh- questions is a common method of teaching. Difficulty answering wh- questions affects a child academically, linguistically, and socially (Parnell, Amerman, & Hartin, 1986).

■ The inability to interpret figurative language leads to a breakdown in text comprehension, which in turn, can frustrate readers and discourage them from continuing reading tasks, and can cause delays in later language development (Palmer & Brooks, 2004).

Help for Language incorporates these principles and is also based on expert professional practice.

References

American Speech-Language-Hearing Association (ASHA). (2001). *Roles and responsibilities of speech-language pathologists with respect to reading and writing in children and adolescents* [Guidelines]. Retrieved March 18, 2010, from www.asha.org/docs/pdf/GL2001-00062.pdf

McMackin, M.C., & Newton, S.L. (2001). Investigative inferences: Constructing meaning from expository texts. *Reading Horizons, 42*(2), 118-137.

National Reading Panel (NRP). (2000). *Teaching children to read: An evidence-based assessment of the scientific research literature on reading and its implications for reading instruction-Reports of the subgroups.* Retrieved March 18, 2010, from www.nichd.nih.gov/publications/nrp/upload/smallbook_pdf.pdf

Palmer, B.C., & Brooks, M.A. (2004). Reading until the cows come home: Figurative language and reading comprehension. *Journal of Adolescent & Adult Literacy, 47,* 370-379.

Parnell, M.M., Amerman, J.D., & Hartin, R.D. (1986). Responses of language-disordered children to wh- questions. *Language, Speech, and Hearing Services in Schools, 17,* 95-106.

LinguiSystems®

LinguiSystems, Inc.
3100 4th Avenue
East Moline, IL 61244
800-776-4332

FAX: 800-577-4555
Email: service@linguisystems.com
Web: linguisystems.com

Copyright © 2004 LinguiSystems, Inc.

Printed in the U.S.A.

ISBN 10: 0-7606-0547-5
ISBN 13: 978-0-7606-0547-9

About the Author

Andrea M. Lazzari, Ed.D., is a speech-language pathologist for Henrico County Public Schools in Richmond, Virginia. She has also worked in a community clinic and in private practice. She has taught preschool students with disabilities and was Supervisor of Early Childhood Special Education Programs for the state of Virginia. She has also served as a teacher trainer at the college and university levels. *HELP for Language* is Andrea's twenty-second publication with LinguiSystems. She is the author or co-author of several other publications, including *125 Ways to Be a Better Test Taker – Elementary*, *125 Ways to Be a Better Test Taker – Intermediate*, and the *HELP* series. She also developed the *HELP Elementary Test*. When she's not teaching or writing, Andrea serves as leader of Girl Scout Troop 3059 and Pit Crew Chief for her daughter Tamara's Soap Box Derby car.

Acknowledgments

With sincere thanks to Kelly Malone (editor), Jamie Bellagamba (desktop publisher), and Margaret Warner (illustrator).

Table of Contents

Table of Contents, *continued*

Reading and Listening

Applying Language Skills

Introduction

HELP for Language provides speech-language pathologists, teachers, parents, and other facilitators with a framework and materials to help children and adults improve their understanding and expression of abstract language. It is intended for children (age 8 and above) and adults who demonstrate weakness or impairment in processing abstract or ambiguous language.

Abstractness and ambiguity are pervasive features of daily communication. Each day, we are required to "read between the lines" of oral language. We must make inferences from minimal communication segments, draw conclusions from inadequate information, discriminate among multiple meanings of words, choose between literal and non-literal meanings, and extrapolate useful from irrelevant information. Each of these skills must be applied within the context of a communication environment that is rapidly delivered and constantly shifting. Individuals who have not mastered these skills are at a disadvantage in understanding academic materials, performing adequately in the workplace, and interacting smoothly in social situations.

Previous books in the HELP series provide the basis for building concrete language skills. *HELP for Language* fills the gap in available materials to support clients with weaknesses in abstract language processing. This book scaffolds on a strong foundation of basic language skills, enabling clients to develop and apply higher-order thinking and reasoning skills.

As with each book in the HELP series, *HELP for Language* takes a no-frills approach to language development and remediation. Skilled clinical judgment is needed to match tasks with each client's needs and to expand each lesson to reflect each client's individual background and interests. The following guidelines will help you effectively use the tasks in *HELP for Language*:

- Begin by identifying the individual's present level of performance, using the person's strengths as a basis for remediating her weaknesses.

- Choose tasks that are relevant to the client's communication needs and functional communication profile.

- Select tasks and items within tasks to enable an individual to gain new skills without being overwhelmed by the difficulty of the tasks. The tasks within each of the four sections and the items within each task are presented with a gradual increase in complexity.

Introduction, *continued*

- Use your own judgment in presenting the tasks orally or as worksheets. If you give tasks for homework, keep in mind that the purpose of homework is review and reinforcement. It's better to introduce and provide practice with new tasks and items in a therapy setting.

- Present materials at a pace that matches the client's rate of acquisition, factoring in repetition for mastery.

- Relate the material to each client's real-world experiences, striving to help the client achieve carryover of target skills to daily communication.

- An answer key has been provided for most of the tasks. Suggested answers have been given for most of the items; however, many answers may be acceptable. Accept any reasonable responses your clients may give, as long as they back them up with appropriate reasoning.

"After all is said and done," I am "pleased as punch" to present *HELP for Language*. I hope that it helps you "hit the ground running" and enables your clients to "make tracks" toward becoming "top-notch" communicators.

Andrea

Answering and Asking Questions
Task A: Who Questions

Answer each question. The first one is done for you.

1. Who saves people who are drowning?

2. Who rides in a stroller?

3. Who is in charge of a sports team?

4. Who rides horses in a rodeo?

5. Who takes care of sick people?

6. Who performs tricks in the circus?

7. Who is the leader of a club?

8. Who directs traffic?

9. Who cares for young children when their parents go out for the evening?

10. Who is in charge of the students and teachers in a school?

11. Who travels in a rocket?

12. Who brings you your food in a restaurant?

13. Who helps her classmates cross the street or get on the bus?

14. Who looks for clues to solve mysteries?

15. Who performs in a movie?

16. Who buys items in a store?

17. Who lives next door to you?

18. Who studies and takes classes?

19. Who plants and harvests crops?

20. Who traveled west in covered wagons?

21. Who rides a bus, train, or airplane?

lifeguard

Baby
coach
Cowboy
Doctor
Clown
President
Poles

I.E.P. Objective: The client will answer "who" questions with 90% or greater accuracy.

Answer each question.

22. Who sits in the stands and cheers loudly for her team? _____

23. Who runs slowly through the park for exercise? _____

24. Who is in charge of a ship? _____

25. Who rings up purchases and makes change in a store? _____

26. Who claps for the actors in a play? _____

27. Who swims underwater with the help of special breathing equipment? _____

28. Who grows up to be a grandmother? _____

29. Who was born on the same day and year as his brother or sister? _____

30. Who is in his or her last year of high school or college? _____

31. Who wears a uniform and completes tasks in different areas to earn badges? _____

32. Who is older than twelve and younger than twenty? _____

33. Who leads an orchestra? _____

34. Who makes cakes, pies, bread, and cookies? _____

35. Who performs tricks and makes things disappear? _____

36. Who hauls loads long distances on the interstate highways? _____

37. Who speaks in rhythm to music on a CD? _____

38. Who digs minerals or gems from under the ground? _____

39. Who is in charge of a state's government? _____

40. Who represents his or her state in Congress? _____

I.E.P. Objective: The client will answer "who" questions with 90% or greater accuracy.

Answering and Asking Questions
Task B: What Questions

Answer each question. The first one is done for you.

1. What flies? _____bird_____

2. What hops? _____

3. What bounces? _____

4. What has leaves? _____

5. What has stripes? _____

6. What ticks? _____

7. What has petals? _____

8. What floats? _____

9. What boils? _____

10. What has pockets? _____

11. What has drawers? _____

12. What freezes? _____

13. What spins? _____

14. What chirps? _____

15. What opens and shuts? _____

16. What has whiskers? _____

17. What has a brake? _____

18. What has cushions? _____

19. What cracks? _____

20. What measures? _____

21. What grows? _____

22. What has a check-out counter? _____

23. What has seats? _____

24. What has lanes? _____

25. What has a glossary? _____

26. What has an on/off switch? _____

27. What has a hard drive? _____

28. What has a heel? _____

29. What has a child-proof lid? _____

30. What stains? _____

31. What twinkles? _____

32. What sprouts? _____

33. What lassos? _____

34. What wrinkles? _____

35. What changes? _____

36. What rises and falls? _____

37. What has scales? _____

38. What has a filter? _____

39. What has a lining? _____

40. What has a pantry? _____

I.E.P. Objective: The client will answer "what" questions with 90% or greater accuracy.

Task C: What Would Happen If Questions

Answer each question. The first one is done for you.

1. What would happen if there were holes in the fish tank?

    All the water would leak out and the fish would die.

2. What would happen if you sat on a wet swing?

3. What would happen if everyone talked loudly in the movie theater?

4. What would happen if you forgot to put the plug in the drain when washing dishes?

5. What would happen if you put dinner in the oven but forgot to turn the oven on?

6. What would happen if there were no trash cans at amusement parks?

7. What would happen if everyone in a rowboat sat on the same side?

8. What would happen if you put away a flashlight without turning it off?

9. What would happen if students didn't write their names on their papers before turning them in to the teacher?

10. What would happen if there was ink on your eraser?

11. What would happen if four boys in one classroom had the same first name?

12. What would happen if you gave a baby a piece of chewing gum?

13. What would happen if you left a chocolate bar in your jacket pocket and then put the jacket in the laundry?

I.E.P. Objective: The client will answer "what would happen if" questions with 90% or greater accuracy.

10

Task C: What Would Happen If Questions, *continued*

Answer each question.

14. What would happen if you were sprinkling salt on your dinner and the lid fell off the saltshaker?

_____

15. What would happen if the screen door had a big hole in it?

_____

16. What would happen if a cat walked across the floor you had just painted?

_____

17. What would happen if there were no safety harnesses on a roller coaster that loops upside down?

_____

18. What would happen if you put jelly on the bread before you put the bread in the toaster?

_____

19. What would happen if it rained hard all day and the team played a football game that evening?

_____

20. What would happen if you tried to pick up a plastic ring with a magnet?

_____

21. What would happen if you got mixed up and put the milk in the cupboard and the cereal in the refrigerator?

_____

22. What would happen if birds didn't fly south in the winter?

_____

23. What would happen if the mail were delivered only once a week?

_____

24. What would happen if alligators and ducks were in the same pond at the zoo?

_____

25. What would happen if you used a tennis racket as an oar?

_____

26. What would happen if you could make only right turns on your bicycle?

_____

I.E.P. Objective: The client will answer "what would happen if" questions with 90% or greater accuracy.

11

Task C: What Would Happen If Questions, *continued*

Answer each question.

27.   What would happen if you tried to light a fire with damp wood?

_____

28.   What would happen if shoes were made only in sizes small and large?

_____

29.   What would happen if every locker had the same combination?

_____

30.   What would happen if a tow truck broke down while towing a car?

_____

31.   What would happen if umbrellas could not be closed?

_____

32.   What would happen if students went to school only when they chose to attend?

_____

33.   What would happen if you could buy only five items each time you went to the grocery store?

_____

34.   What would happen if you threw a fishing line into the lake without baiting the hook?

_____

35.   What would happen if we didn't use punctuation marks when writing stories?

_____

36.   What would happen if baseball players were allowed only one strike?

_____

37.   What would happen if your contact lens fell in a pot of boiling chili while you were stirring it?

_____

38.   What would happen if there were no dollar bills (ones, fives, tens, etc.), only coins?

_____

39.   What would happen if there were no yellow lights on traffic signals?

_____

I.E.P. Objective: The client will answer "what would happen if" questions with 90% or greater accuracy.

HELP for Language   12

Answering and Asking Questions
Task D: What Could Questions

Answer each question. The first one is done for you.

1. What could you do if you push someone's doorbell but it doesn't ring?
   knock on the door

2. What could a student do if he had math problems for homework but he forgot to bring home his math book?

3. What could you do if you want to make a sandwich but you have only one slice of bread?

4. What could you do if your pants are too big but you don't have a belt?

5. What could you do if you need to feed the cat but the cat food bag is empty?

6. What could you do if the book you wanted to read was checked out of the library?

7. What could a student do if she needed cardboard for a school project but the stores were closed?

8. What could you do if you wanted to play a board game but the dice were missing?

9. What could you do if the window was stuck open and the rain was coming in?

10. What could you do if you went to a birthday party and you forgot to bring the gift?

11. What could you do if you bought new shoes at the store but there was only one shoe in the box when you got home?

12. What could a child do if her tooth got washed down the drain before she could put it under her pillow for the tooth fairy?

I.E.P. Objective: The client will answer "what could" questions with 90% or greater accuracy.

Answer each question.

13. What could you do if you climbed a tree but you couldn't get down?

_____

14. What could a child do if he kicked his ball across the street but his dad told him not to leave the yard for any reason?

_____

15. What could an adult do if it was time to fix dinner but all the power was off in her house or apartment?

_____

16. What could a student do if he broke the arm he uses to write and he had to write a paper for homework?

_____

17. What could you do if your golf ball landed in poison ivy?

_____

18. What could a child do if it was time to leave for school and the elevator in her apartment building was stuck?

_____

19. What could you do if you borrowed your friend's hand-held electronic game but it didn't work when you turned it on?

_____

20. What could you do if you need to walk the dog but you can't find his leash?

_____

21. What could you do if you tried on your friend's ring and it got stuck on your finger?

_____

22. What could you do if the telephone kept ringing while you were trying to take a nap?

_____

23. What could you do if you dropped something during a movie and you couldn't see to pick it up?

_____

24. What could you do if you were marching in a parade and you got a cramp in your foot?

_____

I.E.P. Objective: The client will answer "what could" questions with 90% or greater accuracy.

Task D: What Could Questions, *continued*

Answer each question.

25. What could you do if you wrapped two holiday gifts but you forgot what each package contained before you gave them to your friends?

_____

26. What could you do if the hair stylist cut one side of your hair much shorter than the other side?

_____

27. What could you do if a friend invited you to stay for dinner but she was preparing something you did not like?

_____

28. What could you do if you ordered a plain sandwich and the sandwich you received had mayonnaise on it?

_____

29. What could you do if you need to pound in a nail but you have no hammer?

_____

30. What could you do if you want to play checkers but you have only the board and the black checkers?

_____

31. What could you do if it rained during the night and your tent leaked?

_____

32. What could you do if you got locked outside in your pajamas?

_____

33. What could you do if you accidentally ripped a dollar bill in half?

_____

34. What could you do if your hat blew into the bear's habitat while you were visiting the zoo?

_____

35. What could you do if you were fishing and you dropped your lunch overboard?

_____

36. What could you do if you got off at the wrong bus stop and no more buses were scheduled to stop?

_____

I.E.P. Objective: The client will answer "what could" questions with 90% or greater accuracy.

Task E: When Do/Does Questions

Answer each question. The first one is done for you.

1. When do we turn on a fan? _____*when it is hot*_____

2. When do store employees lock the store doors? _____

3. When do we use a straw? _____

4. When do you say "Cheese"? _____

5. When does an egg break? _____

6. When does the doorbell make a noise? _____

7. When do you make your bed? _____

8. When does a balloon pop? _____

9. When does a rainbow appear in the sky? _____

10. When do children hold hands and walk around in a circle while singing? _____
    _____

11. When do we fasten our seatbelts? _____

12. When do students raise their hands? _____

13. When do several children spend the night together at one child's home? _____
    _____

14. When does a rooster crow? _____

15. When do we say "You're it"? _____

16. When do we say "Happy New Year"? _____

17. When do you say "Aaah"? _____

18. When do you put both hands over your ears? _____

19. When do geese fly south? _____

20. When do we shiver? _____

I.E.P. Objective: The client will answer "when do/does" questions with 90% or greater accuracy.

Task E: When Do/Does Questions, *continued*

Answer each question.

21. When do children leave the school building quickly and line up outside? _____ _____

22. When do bears hibernate? _____

23. When do children make wishes? _____

24. When does the sky get dark during the daytime? _____

25. When does the moon disappear? _____

26. When do birds leave their nests? _____

27. When do red, itchy spots appear on our arms or legs? _____

28. When do we put our hands over our hearts? _____

29. When does someone dial 9-1-1? _____

30. When do you receive change at the store? _____

31. When does an airplane lower its wheels? _____

32. When do forest fires easily start? _____

33. When does a baseball umpire yell, "You're out!"? _____

34. When does the football referee put both arms straight up in the air? _____ _____

35. When does an ambulance travel without turning on its siren? _____

36. When do both the sun and the moon appear in the sky? _____

37. When do you use antiseptic cream? _____

38. When does a car easily skid? _____

39. When do you collect $200 in Monopoly? _____

40. When does the ocean look like glass? _____

I.E.P. Objective: The client will answer "when do/does" questions with 90% or greater accuracy.

Answering and Asking Questions
Task F: When Is/Are Questions

Answer each question. The first one is done for you.

1. When is the only time we use a sled? _when there is snow on the ground_

2. When are schools closed? _____

3. When is it time to cut the grass? _____

4. When are sunglasses helpful? _____

5. When is a child ready for a nap? _____

6. When is it time to throw away a marker? _____

7. When are tree leaves red and orange? _____

8. When is it time to change a lightbulb? _____

9. When is a bad time for your flashlight to break? _____

10. When is it hard to pedal a bicycle? _____

11. When is the best time to fly a kite? _____

12. When is a good time to wear your oldest clothing? _____

13. When is it time to buy new jeans? _____

14. When is popcorn done cooking? _____

15. When is it time to throw away your socks? _____

16. When is a pizza ready to eat? _____

17. When are movie tickets least expensive? _____

18. When is a dictionary helpful? _____

19. When are strawberries ready to be picked? _____

20. When is the table ready to be cleared? _____

21. When is a bad time to play music loudly? _____

I.E.P. Objective: The client will answer "when is/are" questions with 90% or greater accuracy.

Task F: **When Is/Are Questions,** *continued*

Answer each question.

22. When is a good time to turn on the porch light? _____

23. When are homemade cookies black on the bottom? _____

24. When is the sun directly overhead? _____

25. When is the most likely time to see a rainbow? _____

26. When are bananas ripe? _____

27. When is sunrise? _____

28. When are the days shortest? _____

29. When are young children allowed to drive real cars? _____

30. When are the movie previews shown? _____

31. When is the sky pink and purple? _____

32. When is a horserace over? _____

33. When is the best time of day to go fishing? _____

34. When is a spatula helpful? _____

35. When is it okay to push someone? _____

36. When is it time to stop at the gas station? _____

37. When is the anniversary of your birth? _____

38. When is the U.S. Independence Day? _____

39. When is the first day of winter? _____

40. When is it time to abandon a ship? _____

41. When is it dark inside the refrigerator? _____

42. When is it time to buy new tires for your car? _____

I.E.P. Objective: The client will answer "when is/are" questions with 90% or greater accuracy.

Task G: When Should/Shouldn't Questions

Answer each question. The first one is done for you.

1. When should you carry an umbrella? _____*when it looks like rain*_____

2. When should you use shampoo? _____

3. When shouldn't you run in front of the swings? _____

4. When should you wear goggles and flippers? _____

5. When should you put more air in your bicycle tires? _____

6. When shouldn't you fall asleep? _____

7. When should you wear a belt? _____

8. When should you throw away a pencil? _____

9. When shouldn't you run on the sidewalk? _____

10. When should children stay home from school? _____

11. When should you return your library books? _____

12. When shouldn't you touch the stove? _____

13. When should you take off your sunglasses? _____

14. When shouldn't you eat a snack? _____

15. When shouldn't you shake a can of soda? _____

16. When should you buy a new backpack? _____

17. When should you use a paper cup? _____

18. When shouldn't you cross the street? _____

19. When should you wear a parachute? _____

20. When should you throw away a carton of milk? _____

21. When shouldn't you wear flip-flops? _____

I.E.P. Objective: The client will answer "when should/shouldn't" questions with 90% or greater accuracy.

20

Task G: When Should/Shouldn't Questions, *continued*

Answer each question.

22. When should a driver stop the car? _____

23. When should you use a dictionary? _____

24. When shouldn't you chew gum? _____

25. When should you stop, drop, and roll? _____

26. When shouldn't you open the front door? _____

27. When should you whisper? _____

28. When should you hold your breath? _____

29. When shouldn't you take something from the oven? _____

30. When should you turn to a new page on the calendar? _____

31. When should you duck? _____

32. When shouldn't you open a letter? _____

33. When shouldn't you yell? _____

34. When should you hang up the telephone? _____

35. When should you break a window? _____

36. When should you remain perfectly still? _____

37. When should you use an uppercase letter? _____

38. When shouldn't you stand outside in an open field? _____

39. When should you interrupt someone who is talking? _____

40. When should you save your work on the computer? _____

41. When shouldn't you leave a campfire? _____

42. When shouldn't you pull a ripcord? _____

I.E.P. Objective: The client will answer "when should/shouldn't" questions with 90% or greater accuracy.

Task H: Where Questions

Answer each question. The first one is done for you.

1. Where does the line leader stand? _____*at the front of the line*_____

2. Where do people get on and off a train? _____

3. Where do a queen and king live? _____

4. Where do we keep ice cream? _____

5. Where do people use a menu? _____

6. Where do polar bears live? _____

7. Where should you place your napkin while eating? _____

8. Where would you take a sick pet? _____

9. Where would you look to find the index to a book? _____

10. Where are your feet if you are doing a handstand? _____

11. Where do caterpillars rest before they become butterflies? _____

12. Where are operations performed? _____

13. Where would you find an apple's core? _____

14. Where is a caboose located? _____

15. Where do people sit in rows of seats in the dark? _____

16. Where do the roots of a plant grow? _____

17. Where can you find many stores that are under one roof? _____

18. Where does the President of the United States live? _____

19. Where do you check in and receive a key? _____

20. Where would you go to walk on a boardwalk? _____

21. Where are your lungs? _____

I.E.P. Objective: The client will answer "where" questions with 90% or greater accuracy.

22

Task H: Where Questions, *continued*

Answer each question.

22. Where do cacti grow? _____

23. Where would you see a fifty-yard line? _____

24. Where is the equator located? _____

25. Where can you go to see paintings and statues? _____

26. Where is the *Titanic* located? _____

27. Where does lava come from? _____

28. Where do water lilies grow? _____

29. Where would you find stethoscopes and thermometers? _____

30. Where can you go to see a silo and a plow? _____

31. Where can you find a hard drive and a monitor? _____

32. Where do men wear tuxedos? _____

33. Where would you see a checkered flag waved? _____

34. Where can you find a carburetor and spark plugs? _____

35. Where are airplanes stored when they are not being used? _____

36. Where can you buy an almanac? _____

37. Where is a safety deposit box located? _____

38. Where would you go to see wild animals in captivity? _____

39. Where are saltwater pearls generally formed? _____

40. Where should you aim to hit the bull's-eye? _____

41. Where do people drive on the left side of the road? _____

42. Where do X-ray technicians work? _____

I.E.P. Objective: The client will answer "where" questions with 90% or greater accuracy.

Answering and Asking Questions
Task I: Which Questions

Choose the best answer for each question. The first one is done for you.

1. Which is a quicker way of traveling a long distance, a bus or
    a train?   *train*

2. Which tastes better on a hamburger, ketchup or syrup?   _____

3. Which has holes punched in the side, notebook paper or
    a newspaper?   _____

4. Which activity requires two people, climbing a tree or
    playing Ping-Pong?   _____

5. Which vehicle holds the most passengers, a car or a van?   _____

6. Which is easier to learn to ride, a skateboard or a scooter?   _____

7. Which can you buy in a bakery, pies or pickles?   _____

8. Which is a better picnic food, soup or sandwiches?   _____

9. Which is less expensive, a school lunch or a movie ticket?   _____

10. Which is a better game for a person with a broken finger,
    soccer or volleyball?   _____

11. Which is a better place to hide money, in a glass jar or
    a wooden box?   _____

12. Which is a healthier snack, raisins or gumdrops?   _____

13. Which animal is easier to tame, a cheetah or a donkey?   _____

14. Which are better shoes for hiking, boots or sandals?   _____

15. Which takes less time, making your bed or
    hanging up your jacket?   _____

16. Which animal is quieter, a rabbit or a parrot?   _____

17. Which is a more comfortable place to nap, on a plank or
    in a hammock?   _____

18. Which time of day are more people awake, noon or midnight?   _____

19. Which are you more likely to find in a toolbox,
    pliers or quarters?   _____

20. Which are made from grapes, plums or raisins?   _____

I.E.P. Objective: The client will choose answers to "which" questions with 90% or greater accuracy.

Choose the best answer for each question.

21. Which can you find beneath the sea, a rink or a reef? _____

22. Which helps a student complete her homework, a calendar or a calculator? _____

23. Which is more pleasant, a visit to the dentist or a visit to an aquarium? _____

24. Which is a better place to hide, in a tree or behind a stool? _____

25. Which is harder to do, climb a rope or slide down a pole? _____

26. Which is a sign of fall, blossoms on the trees or pumpkins on the vine? _____

27. Which sport requires more equipment, basketball or football? _____

28. Which bounces higher, a croquet ball or a tennis ball? _____

29. Which instrument is more difficult to play, drums or a violin? _____

30. Which is more soothing, rap music or a lullaby? _____

31. Which is noisier, a helicopter or a motorcycle? _____

32. Which is a better name for a football team, the Hurricanes or the Snowflakes? _____

33. Which is a better gift for someone you don't know very well, a plant or a shirt? _____

34. Which holds more people, a terrarium or a stadium? _____

35. Which activity requires more strength, rowing or fishing? _____

36. Which person is fictional, Johnny Appleseed or Mary Poppins? _____

37. Which is the best material for building a raft, straw or wood? _____

38. Which is a better apartment for a family with a two-year old, bottom floor or top floor? _____

39. Which is a better job for a person who is blind, a teacher or a firefighter? _____

40. Which is flammable, a screw or a match? _____

I.E.P. Objective: The client will choose answers to "which" questions with 90% or greater accuracy.

HELP for Language   25

Answering and Asking Questions
Task J: Why Do/Does Questions

Answer each question. The first one is done for you.

1. Why do airplanes have wheels?

   so they can taxi down runways

2. Why do we peel bananas before eating them?

3. Why do drawers have knobs?

4. Why do roads have lines painted down the middle?

5. Why does a monkey have a long tail?

6. Why does a lamp have a shade?

7. Why do ink pens have lids?

8. Why do you use a long fork when cooking over a grill?

9. Why do eggs come in cartons?

10. Why do front doors have peepholes?

11. Why do schools have flagpoles?

12. Why do fire trucks have long ladders?

13. Why do you write your address on a package before mailing it?

I.E.P. Objective: The client will answer "why do/does" questions with 90% or greater accuracy.

Task J: Why Do/Does Questions, *continued*

Answer each question.

14. Why do some people cry during movies?

_____

15. Why do most people use saddles when horseback riding?

_____

16. Why do garbage trucks beep when backing up?

_____

17. Why do skyscrapers have elevators?

_____

18. Why do speed skaters wear helmets?

_____

19. Why do buckets have handles?

_____

20. Why do medicine bottles have childproof caps?

_____

21. Why do we grease a pan before pouring in the cake batter?

_____

22. Why do art museums have guards?

_____

23. Why do cars have mirrors on the sides?

_____

24. Why do television shows have commercials?

_____

25. Why do some shovels have pointed ends?

_____

26. Why do camels have humps?

_____

I.E.P. Objective: The client will answer "why do/does" questions with 90% or greater accuracy.

Answer each question.

27. Why do belts have more than one hole?

_____

28. Why do limousines have dark windows?

_____

29. Why does everyone have a different telephone number?

_____

30. Why do all the cards in a deck have the same design on the back?

_____

31. Why do you need to punch in a pin number before using an automatic teller machine?

_____

32. Why do dentists wear gloves?

_____

33. Why do we plow the ground before planting seeds?

_____

34. Why do we recycle aluminum cans?

_____

35. Why do we turn off car engines when filling the gas tank?

_____

36. Why do we set our clocks back an hour in the fall?

_____

37. Why do we lower the American flag at dusk?

_____

38. Why do bees always return to the same hive?

_____

39. Why do hourglasses (timers) have a narrow part in the middle?

_____

I.E.P. Objective: The client will answer "why do/does" questions with 90% or greater accuracy.

Task K: Why Don't/Doesn't Questions

Answer each question. Begin your answers with the word *because*. The first one is done for you.

1. Why don't we swim while wearing a sweatshirt?

    because a wet sweatshirt is heavy and would make it difficult to swim

2. Why don't we play baseball indoors?

3. Why don't we sleep in our clothing?

4. Why don't we use many blankets in the summertime?

5. Why don't we wash our hands in boiling water?

6. Why don't we keep butter in the pantry?

7. Why don't teachers like their students to chew gum in class?

8. Why don't we change a lightbulb while the light is turned on?

9. Why don't roller skating rinks have carpeted floors?

10. Why don't we put rocks under a jungle gym?

11. Why don't running shoes have smooth soles?

12. Why don't six-year-old children baby-sit?

13. Why don't we share toothbrushes?

I.E.P. Objective: The client will answer "why don't/doesn't" questions with 90% or greater accuracy.

Task K: Why Don't/Doesn't Questions, *continued*

Answer each question. Begin your answers with the word *because*.

14. Why don't department stores allow customers to eat food while they shop?

    _____

15. Why don't we leave the car windows down all night?

    _____

16. Why don't ice-cream cones have more than three scoops of ice cream?

    _____

17. Why don't theaters leave the lights on during the movie?

    _____

18. Why don't we pick apples in the summer?

    _____

19. Why don't basketball players wear shoes with cleats?

    _____

20. Why don't piano players march in the school band?

    _____

21. Why don't we use a rake to clear snow off the walkway?

    _____

22. Why don't dogs take themselves for walks?

    _____

23. Why don't turkeys fly south for the winter?

    _____

24. Why don't we eat dessert first?

    _____

25. Why don't people in Nebraska mow their lawns during the winter?

    _____

26. Why don't we dial 9-1-1 if our car runs out of gas?

    _____

I.E.P. Objective: The client will answer "why don't/doesn't" questions with 90% or greater accuracy.

30

Task K: Why Don't/Doesn't Questions, *continued*

Answer each question. Begin your answers with the word *because*.

27. Why doesn't the store sell cigarettes to people younger than 18?

_____

28. Why don't airplanes fly in ice storms?

_____

29. Why don't birds build nests of stones?

_____

30. Why doesn't a person use the motor on a sailboat on most days?

_____

31. Why doesn't a train stop in each town it passes through?

_____

32. Why don't people play golf during a thunderstorm?

_____

33. Why don't people use the elevator to exit a building during a fire?

_____

34. Why don't we use bleach when washing our blue jeans?

_____

35. Why don't we swim in the ocean at night?

_____

36. Why don't foxes have gills?

_____

37. Why don't elephants live in the mountains?

_____

38. Why don't desert plants have large leaves?

_____

39. Why don't the back doors of police cars open from the inside?

_____

I.E.P. Objective: The client will answer "why don't/doesn't" questions with 90% or greater accuracy.

Task L: How Do/Does Questions

Answer each question. The first one is done for you.

1. How does a baby feel?   *soft*

2. How does a whisper sound?

3. How does an icicle feel?

4. How does icing taste?

5. How does a needle feel?

6. How does a turtle move?

7. How does a monster look?

8. How does a lollipop feel after you lick it?

9. How does thunder sound?

10. How does garbage smell after one week?

11. How do clothes feel when the dryer stops?

12. How do your shoes look after running through mud?

13. How does a dog look wearing a hat and a bowtie?

14. How does a bowling ball feel?

15. How does the kitchen look before you wash the dishes?

16. How do children feel the morning after a slumber party?

17. How do you feel after winning $50 in a contest?

18. How does a piece of paper look after you have squashed it in your hand?

19. How do potato chips sound when you chew them?

20. How does sandpaper feel?

21. How does lemonade taste without sugar?

I.E.P. Objective: The client will answer "how do/does" questions with 90% or greater accuracy.

HELP for Language   32

Task L: How Do/Does Questions, *continued*

Answer each question.

22. How does a metal railing feel in the summer? _____

23. How does sea water taste? _____

24. How do brownies smell when they are baking? _____

25. How does a child feel when she has nobody to play with? _____

26. How does a snakeskin feel? _____

27. How does a sunset look? _____

28. How do you feel after striking out in softball? _____

29. How do your arms feel after rowing a boat all day? _____

30. How does a student feel when he gets a good grade
     on an assignment? _____

31. How does a raw egg feel if you break it in your hand? _____

32. How does paper look if you glue glitter on it? _____

33. How does the bathroom mirror look after you've taken
     a hot shower? _____

34. How does a jar look after you've eaten the last olive? _____

35. How does a shirt look after someone has ironed it? _____

36. How does sunlight look when it reflects off the snow? _____

37. How do a hummingbird's wings move? _____

38. How does the Statue of Liberty look if you are standing
     at the bottom? _____

39. How does a horse look after someone has ridden it across
     the desert? _____

40. How do leaves feel a week after they have fallen from the tree? _____

I.E.P. Objective: The client will answer "how do/does" questions with 90% or greater accuracy.

33

Answering and Asking Questions
Task M: How Do You Know Questions

Answer each question. The first one is done for you.

1. How do you know if someone is calling you on the telephone?

    The telephone rings.

2. How do you know if it rained overnight?

    _____

3. How do you know if your socks are dirty?

    _____

4. How do you know if you forgot to close the lid on the play dough?

    _____

5. How do you know if your teacher is absent?

    _____

6. How do you know if the microwave is done cooking?

    _____

7. How do you know if the lawn needs mowed?

    _____

8. How do you know if the car needs gas?

    _____

9. How do you know if the trash has been picked up?

    _____

10. How do you know if you've dialed the wrong number?

    _____

11. How do you know if the rug needs to be vacuumed?

    _____

12. How do you know if the freezer is broken?

    _____

13. How do you know when your library book is due?

    _____

I.E.P. Objective: The client will answer "how do you know" questions with 90% or greater accuracy.

Task M: How Do You Know Questions, *continued*

Answer each question.

14. How does a child know that he has gotten taller?

_____

15. How do you know if your neighbors are on vacation?

_____

16. How do you know if you've cooked your toast too long?

_____

17. How do you know if the ice-cream truck is coming?

_____

18. How do you know when the mail carrier has picked up your mail?

_____

19. How do you know if you bowled a strike?

_____

20. How do you know if the ice in your juice has melted?

_____

21. How do you know if someone has just taken a shower?

_____

22. How do you know if your raft has a hole in it?

_____

23. How do you know if you're late for dinner?

_____

24. How do you know if your blue jeans have been washed?

_____

25. How do you know if a tree is dead?

_____

26. How do you know if your watch has stopped?

_____

I.E.P. Objective: The client will answer "how do you know" questions with 90% or greater accuracy.

Task M: How Do You Know Questions, *continued*

Answer each question.

27. How do you know if school has been cancelled because of bad weather?

_____

28. How do you know if the driver of a car has children?

_____

29. How do you know if you are getting sick?

_____

30. How do you know if a thunderstorm is getting close?

_____

31. How do you know if a match has been used?

_____

32. How do you know if birds have hatched?

_____

33. How do you know when a movie is over?

_____

34. How do you know spring has arrived?

_____

35. How do you know if your scissors need sharpened?

_____

36. How do you know if you are looking at Sunday's newspaper?

_____

37. How do you know if a traffic light is broken?

_____

38. How do you know if a store is about to close?

_____

39. How do you know if a postage stamp has been used?

_____

I.E.P. Objective: The client will answer "how do you know" questions with 90% or greater accuracy.

36

Task N: If Questions

Answer each question with a *yes* or *no* response. The first one is done for you.

1. If the doorbell is ringing is there someone at the door?   _____*yes*_____

2. If someone is snoring, is he asleep? _____

3. If you're wearing a bracelet, do you have on jewelry? _____

4. If a child is cranky, is he in a good mood? _____

5. If you've finished your drink, is your glass full? _____

6. If you turn up the volume on the TV, will it get louder? _____

7. If you put your hands on your knees, are you touching your legs? _____

8. If you leap in the air, do your feet leave the ground? _____

9. If you got a splinter in the bottom of your foot, were you wearing shoes? _____

10. If a horse crosses the finish line third, is it the winner? _____

11. If the traffic light is yellow, should you speed up? _____

12. If there is dirt on the lettuce, should you throw it away? _____

13. If your bicycle tire has a leak, should you get a new tire? _____

14. If you weed the vegetable garden, should you pull up the tomato plants? _____

15. If soup is lukewarm, is it cool enough to eat? _____

16. If you ride a scooter, do your legs go around in circles? _____

17. If a letter has been shredded, can you read it? _____

18. If a boat is tied securely to the dock, will it drift away? _____

19. If you recline your chair, are you leaning forward? _____

20. If you have sixty cents, do you have more than a half dollar? _____

I.E.P. Objective: The client will answer "if" questions with 90% or greater accuracy.

Task N: If Questions, *continued*

Answer each question with a *yes* or *no* response.

21. If you cut a ball in half, will you have two equal pieces? _____

22. If you skin your knee, should you go to the emergency room? _____

23. If you throw newspapers in the garbage can, will they get recycled? _____

24. If the sea is rough, is it a good day for surfing? _____

25. If the coals are glowing, is the fire out? _____

26. If you feel drowsy, are you ready to fall asleep? _____

27. If every desk in a classroom is occupied, is anyone absent? _____

28. If an animal has a skeleton, does it have bones? _____

29. If a bill is overdue, have you paid it? _____

30. If someone received the most votes, did he win the election? _____

31. If a peach is soft when you bite into it, is it ripe? _____

32. If you live near the equator, do you live in a cold climate? _____

33. If the game ends in a tie, did your team score the most points? _____

34. If the sun is setting, is it evening? _____

35. If it is harvest time, is it spring? _____

36. If you win first place in a competition, do you get a silver medal? _____

37. If you leave an ice cube in the sun, will it evaporate? _____

38. If it is rush hour, is there a lot of traffic? _____

39. If you live in the United States, do you live in South America? _____

40. If you fold a square of paper in half twice, will you have a smaller square? _____

I.E.P. Objective: The client will answer "if" questions with 90% or greater accuracy.

38

Task O: Responding to True/False Statements

Tell if each statement is true or false. If a statement is false, tell why. The first one is done for you.

1. Bricks are strong building materials. *true*_____

2. If water gets too hot it will freeze. _____

3. A moped can go faster than a car. _____

4. A pinwheel spins easily in the breeze. _____

5. A dime is worth more than a nickel. _____

6. Daisies have thorns. _____

7. Subways run on underground tracks. _____

8. Sun visors cover the top of your head. _____

9. Stale crackers are crisp. _____

10. The best place to walk your dog is in the middle of the road. _____
_____

11. Spiders live in hives. _____

12. Piano keys are black or white. _____

13. Lifting weights will build up your muscles. _____

14. Marbles are made of glass. _____

15. You can play outside longer in the summertime. _____

16. A globe is a model of the sun. _____

17. Drivers should stop their cars on the railroad tracks to look for trains. _____
_____

18. In baseball, you run to first base after you strike out. _____

19. A compass shows which direction is north. _____

20. If you take the next to the last muffin, there will be one left. _____

I.E.P. Objective: The client will respond to true/false statements with 90% or greater accuracy.

39

Task O: Responding to True/False Statements, *continued*

Tell if each statement is true or false. If a statement is false, tell why.

21. A pencil breaks more easily than a pen. _____

22. A racecar's tires are changed during a pit stop. _____

23. A young duck is called a gosling. _____

24. You can use cell phones only when you are outside. _____

25. There is only one correct answer to each addition problem. _____

26. A triangle has more sides than a rectangle. _____

27. A group of nine children can form two even teams. _____

28. A postage stamp is smaller than a credit card. _____

29. Ice hockey is more dangerous to play than golf. _____

30. A baby polar bear is called a papoose. _____

31. Glass ornaments are fragile. _____

32. Statues are motionless. _____

33. You can erase ink from a permanent marker. _____

34. Dry towels are heavier than wet towels. _____

35. You can measure weight in pounds. _____

36. We read from right to left. _____

37. A computer keyboard contains five vowels. _____

38. There are four colors in the U.S. flag. _____

39. Silver is worth more than gold. _____

40. Gasoline is a flammable liquid. _____

I.E.P. Objective: The client will respond to true/false statements with 90% or greater accuracy.

Task P: Formulating Questions

Imagine each item is the response to a question. Read each response. Then make up a question that could go with the response. The first one is done for you.

1. Put it on the table. *Where should I put your book?*

2. The meeting is next Tuesday. _____

3. Andy was in front of Roger. _____

4. Yes, I'd love to go! _____

5. It's mine. _____

6. I was outside. _____

7. Yes, you may. _____

8. The extra books are in the box. _____

9. I'm sure I gave it to you. _____

10. I turned it off because no one was watching it. _____

11. I saw your bicycle parked out front. _____

12. No, I don't think so. _____

13. Sit in between Jan and Bonnie. _____

14. Of course I'm disappointed! _____

15. I recognized your voice. _____

16. Count me out! _____

17. That would be great! _____

18. anytime after Friday _____

19. under the porch _____

20. because someone left the door open _____

I.E.P. Objective: When presented with answers, the client will formulate matching questions with 90% or greater accuracy.

41

Task P: Formulating Questions, *continued*

Imagine each item is the response to a question. Read each response. Then make up a question that could go with the response.

21. the girl with the long hair _____

22. because it was rotten _____

23. until five o'clock _____

24. once in a while _____

25. Davy Crockett _____

26. when the buzzer sounds _____

27. never _____

28. $1.95 _____

29. well, maybe _____

30. 72 _____

31. 85 degrees _____

32. D _____

33. strawberry _____

34. brown and white _____

35. eight pounds _____

36. Mr. Griffith _____

37. 125 miles _____

38. only if they're done _____

39. until he starts barking _____

40. absolutely not _____

I.E.P. Objective: When presented with answers, the client will formulate matching questions with 90% or greater accuracy.

Describing Objects and Defining Words
Task A: Identifying Functions of Objects

Name two things you can do with each object. The first one is done for you.

1. pencil _____*write, draw*_____

2. glass of water _____

3. rope _____

4. stick _____

5. ball _____

6. paper sack _____

7. wagon _____

8. cardboard box _____

9. clothespin _____

10. axe _____

11. transparent tape _____

12. pumpkin _____

13. milk carton _____

14. Ziplock® bag _____

15. blanket _____

16. chair _____

17. rubber band _____

18. magazine _____

19. flower _____

20. egg _____

21. paper towel _____

I.E.P. Objective: The client will identify functions of common objects with 90% or greater accuracy.

Describing Objects and Defining Words
Task A: Identifying Functions of Objects, *continued*

Name two things you can do with each object.

22. ribbon _____

23. ruler _____

24. hula hoop _____

25. net _____

26. penny _____

27. straw _____

28. flower pot _____

29. brick _____

30. sponge _____

31. newspaper _____

32. apple _____

33. envelope _____

34. aluminum foil _____

35. screwdriver _____

36. bandana _____

37. sock _____

38. cracker _____

39. yarn _____

40. log _____

41. flag _____

42. dictionary _____

I.E.P. Objective: The client will identify functions of common objects with 90% or greater accuracy.

Describing Objects and Defining Words
Task B: Naming Objects Identified by Two Attributes

Name an object to fit each description. The first one is done for you.

1.	round and black	_checker_	21.	beautiful and colorful	_____
2.	cool and sweet	_____	22.	pink and fluffy	_____
3.	small and round	_____	23.	clear and breakable	_____
4.	big and strong	_____	24.	sharp and metal	_____
5.	cute and furry	_____	25.	wet and slippery	_____
6.	cold and white	_____	26.	dirty and smelly	_____
7.	big and dark	_____	27.	cold and hard	_____
8.	big and yellow	_____	28.	yellow and waterproof	_____
9.	shiny and red	_____	29.	deep and wide	_____
10.	dark and scary	_____	30.	rough and sharp	_____
11.	sweet and juicy	_____	31.	old and worn	_____
12.	red and liquid	_____	32.	sour and green	_____
13.	round and light	_____	33.	brown and liquid	_____
14.	silver and round	_____	34.	sticky and lumpy	_____
15.	sharp and long	_____	35.	sweet and brown	_____
16.	soft and light	_____	36.	tiny and annoying	_____
17.	loud and heavy	_____	37.	hot and greasy	_____
18.	round and green	_____	38.	fragrant and thorny	_____
19.	red and hot	_____	39.	clear and blue	_____
20.	white and wooly	_____	40.	difficult and long	_____

I.E.P. Objective: The client will name objects identified by two attributes with 90% or greater accuracy.

Describing Objects and Defining Words
Task C: Identifying Actions Associated with Objects

Tell what each object can do. The first one is done for you.

1. What can a whistle do? _____ *make noise* _____

2. What can scissors do? _____

3. What can a flashlight do? _____

4. What can a telephone do? _____

5. What can a bubble do? _____

6. What can a wheel do? _____

7. What can a sponge do? _____

8. What can a parrot do? _____

9. What can goggles do? _____

10. What can a merry-go-round do? _____

11. What can a cow do? _____

12. What can a kite do? _____

13. What can a kangaroo do? _____

14. What can a skateboard do? _____

15. What can a paperweight do? _____

16. What can a leash do? _____

17. What can gloves do? _____

18. What can an elevator do? _____

19. What can a shoe do? _____

20. What can a basket do? _____

21. What can a bandage do? _____

I.E.P. Objective: The client will identify actions associated with common objects with 90% or greater accuracy.

Task C: Identifying Actions Associated with Objects, *continued*

Tell what each object can do.

22. What can a hatchet do? _____

23. What can a helmet do? _____

24. What can a blender do? _____

25. What can elastic do? _____

26. What can a clothespin do? _____

27. What can a lighthouse do? _____

28. What can a chain do? _____

29. What can a plow do? _____

30. What can a coupon do? _____

31. What can a window blind do? _____

32. What can a thermometer do? _____

33. What can crutches do? _____

34. What can sunscreen do? _____

35. What can vitamins do? _____

36. What can antiseptic do? _____

37. What can a windmill do? _____

38. What can a computer mouse do? _____

39. What can a motor do? _____

40. What can a suction cup do? _____

41. What can a conveyer belt do? _____

42. What can a generator do? _____

I.E.P. Objective: The client will identify actions associated with common objects with 90% or greater accuracy.

Task D: Responding to Action/Agent Statements

Tell if each statement is true or false.

1. Oranges jingle. _____*false*_____   21. Shovels stitch. _____

2. Dogs growl. _____   22. Pens boil. _____

3. Bells drive. _____   23. Socks shine. _____

4. Umbrellas protect. _____   24. Fish trot. _____

5. Clouds drift. _____   25. Jackets zip. _____

6. Computers smile. _____   26. Rakes ring. _____

7. Balls roll. _____   27. Babies drool. _____

8. Bathtubs chirp. _____   28. Helicopters hover. _____

9. Rugs crawl. _____   29. Easels chop. _____

10. Grasshoppers holler. _____   30. Seeds sprout. _____

11. Children joke. _____   31. Winners celebrate. _____

12. Donkeys kick. _____   32. Movies entertain. _____

13. Birds migrate. _____   33. Lanterns slice. _____

14. Leaves melt. _____   34. Cold water refreshes. _____

15. Paint drips. _____   35. Fire scorches. _____

16. Lights flicker. _____   36. Artists illustrate. _____

17. Pillows point. _____   37. Mud rumbles. _____

18. Pans cry. _____   38. Medicine heals. _____

19. Crabs dig. _____   39. Roads evaporate. _____

20. Glass sparkles. _____   40. Judges sentence. _____

I.E.P. Objective: The client will determine if action/agent statements are true or false with 90% or greater accuracy.

Describing Objects and Defining Words
Task E: Identifying Actions Not Associated with Objects

Choose the best answer for each question. The first one is done for you.

1. What can't a toaster do, ring or pop? _____ *ring* _____

2. What can't a clock do, tick or tweet? _____

3. What can't soap do, clean or beep? _____

4. What can't a grasshopper do, shout or hop? _____

5. What can't a marble do, mark or roll? _____

6. What can't a dog do, stretch or sketch? _____

7. What can't a piece of wire do, whistle or bend? _____

8. What can't a balloon do, pop or chop? _____

9. What can't a faucet do, drip or blink? _____

10. What can't a candle do, bark or melt? _____

11. What can't a cat do, neigh or pounce? _____

12. What can't a door do, slam or rise? _____

13. What can't a kite do, bounce or fly? _____

14. What can't a raft do, float or scream? _____

15. What can't the sun do, set or pack? _____

16. What can't a ruler do, print or measure? _____

17. What can't a penguin do, gallop or waddle? _____

18. What can't a snake do, march or slither? _____

19. What can't a music CD do, spin or trim? _____

20. What can't a rosebud do, rinse or bloom? _____

21. What can't a traffic light do, blink or cheer? _____

I.E.P. Objective: The client will identify actions not associated with common objects with 90% or greater
accuracy.

Task E: Identifying Actions Not Associated with Objects, *continued*

Choose the best answer for each question.

22. What can't a plow do, dig or add? _____

23. What can't a tree do, skip or bend? _____

24. What can't a bell do, chime or creep? _____

25. What can't a spider do, spin or punch? _____

26. What can't a brush do, paint or climb? _____

27. What can't a pig do, snort or chirp? _____

28. What can't gelatin do, giggle or jiggle? _____

29. What can't a fork do, fold or stab? _____

30. What can't paint do, stew or chip? _____

31. What can't a star do, yell or glow? _____

32. What can't a toothpick do, break or sleep? _____

33. What can't an egg do, reach or hatch? _____

34. What can't a cake do, hope or rise? _____

35. What can't a gate do, latch or curl? _____

36. What can't a newspaper do, inform or enclose? _____

37. What can't a bee do, trot or hover? _____

38. What can't a calculator do, multiply or disinfect? _____

39. What can't a computer mouse do, scamper or click? _____

40. What can't a china teacup do, bend or shatter? _____

41. What can't a marching band do, halt or churn? _____

42. What can't a mirror do, repeat or reflect? _____

I.E.P. Objective: The client will identify actions not associated with common objects with 90% or greater accuracy.

Task F: Combining Positive and Negative Action/Agent Statements

Fill in the blanks to complete each statement. The first one is done for you.

1. A dog can't oink but it can _____ *bark* _____.

2. A fish can't walk but it can _____.

3. An owl can't swim but it can _____.

4. A cow can't hop but it can _____.

5. A frog can't run but it can _____.

6. An ant can't tweet but it can _____.

7. A snake can't gallop but it can _____.

8. A bear can't sting but it can _____.

9. An alligator can't roar but it can _____.

10. A spider can't quack but it can _____.

11. A tiger can't slither but it can _____.

12. A turkey can't fly but it can _____.

13. Eyes can't hear but they can _____.

14. Water can't melt but it can _____.

15. Gelatin can't shatter but it can _____.

16. A car can't _____ but it can race.

17. A refrigerator can't _____ but it can cool.

18. A fire can't _____ but it can burn.

19. A tree can't _____ but it can sway.

20. A marble can't _____ but it can roll.

21. A telephone can't _____ but it can ring.

I.E.P. Objective: The client will complete action/agent statements with 90% or greater accuracy.

Task F: Combining Positive and Negative Action/Agent Statements, *continued*

Fill in the blanks to complete each statement.

22. A broom can't _____ but it can sweep.

23. A door can't _____ but it can slam.

24. A balloon can't _____ but it can pop.

25. A paperclip can't _____ but it can bend.

26. A battery can't _____ but it can power.

27. A mirror can't _____ but it can reflect.

28. A microphone can't _____ but it can amplify.

29. A teapot can't _____ but it can whistle.

30. A horse can't _____ but it can _____.

31. A caterpillar can't _____ but it can _____.

32. A cheetah can't _____ but it can _____.

33. A baby can't _____ but she can _____.

34. A train can't _____ but it can _____.

35. A key can't _____ but it can _____.

36. A drawer can't _____ but it can _____.

37. A pencil can't _____ but it can _____.

38. A computer can't _____ but it can _____.

39. Snow can't _____ but it can _____.

40. Mud can't _____ but it can _____.

41. A satellite can't _____ but it can _____.

42. A mime can't _____ but he can _____.

I.E.P. Objective: The client will complete action/agent statements with 90% or greater accuracy.

Describing Objects and Defining Words
Task G: Using Exclusion to Identify Objects

Think of an item for each statement. The first one is done for you.

1. Name a vegetable that is not green. *corn* _____

2. Name a flower that is not red. _____

3. Name clothing that you do not wear when it is cold outside. _____

4. Name a word that does not rhyme with *boy*. _____

5. Name something you would not put on a sandwich. _____

6. Name something that does not fit in the palm of your hand. _____

7. Name a game that is not difficult to play. _____

8. Name a food that is not spicy. _____

9. Name a vehicle that is not noisy. _____

10. Name something you would not keep in a dresser. _____

11. Name a food you would not eat with a fork. _____

12. Name something you would not find in a classroom. _____

13. Name clothing most people do not wear year-round. _____

14. Name an animal that does not live in/near the sea. _____

15. Name something a baby cannot do. _____

16. Name a place that is not quiet. _____

17. Name a food most people do not eat raw. _____

18. Name something you wouldn't pack in your suitcase. _____

19. Name a food you should not keep in the freezer. _____

20. Name something you should not do in a library. _____

21. Name an animal that you cannot ride. _____

I.E.P. Objective: The client will use exclusion to identify objects with 90% or greater accuracy.

Task G: Using Exclusion to Identify Objects, *continued*

Think of an item for each statement.

22. Name a game in which you do not use dice. _____

23. Name something soccer players do not wear. _____

24. Name a place where an elephant would not fit. _____

25. Name a sport that does not require equipment. _____

26. Name a game for which you do not keep score. _____

27. Name a food that doesn't smell good. _____

28. Name a tool that is not sharp. _____

29. Name something a mail carrier does not deliver. _____

30. Name a holiday on which most people do not go to work. _____

31. Name something you would not see in New York City. _____

32. Name a book your grandmother or grandfather could not have read as a child. _____
_____

33. Name something a magnet would not attract. _____

34. Name a place that is not warm in November. _____

35. Name a character that is not real. _____

36. Name a food George Washington could not have eaten. _____

37. Name something the Pilgrims did not bring to this country. _____

38. Name somewhere Abraham Lincoln could not have gone. _____

39. Name a state that doesn't touch the ocean. _____

40. Name a country that is not in Asia. _____

41. Name an item you would not normally find in a first-aid kit. _____

I.E.P. Objective: The client will use exclusion to identify objects with 90% or greater accuracy.

Describing Objects and Defining Words
Task H: Identifying Similarities and Differences of Objects/Places/Events

Answer each question stating one likeness and one difference for each pair of items. The first one is done for you.

1. How are a bus and a train alike and different? *Both are forms of mass transportation, but a train runs on tracks and a bus drives on the road.*

2. How are apples and peaches alike and different? _____

   _____

3. How are a duck and a turkey alike and different? _____

   _____

4. How are cookies and crackers alike and different? _____

   _____

5. How are fingers and toes alike and different? _____

   _____

6. How are a clock and a watch alike and different? _____

   _____

7. How are a bucket and a bowl alike and different? _____

   _____

8. How are a spoon and a fork alike and different? _____

   _____

9. How are shoes and slippers alike and different? _____

   _____

10. How are a surfboard and a sailboat alike and different? _____

   _____

11. How are a rake and a broom alike and different? _____

   _____

12. How are a gerbil and a chipmunk alike and different? _____

   _____

I.E.P. Objective: The client will identify similarities and differences of objects/places/events with 90% or greater accuracy.

HELP for Language   55

Task H: Identifying Similarities and Differences of Objects/Places/Events, *continued*

Answer each question stating one likeness and one difference for each pair of items.

13. How are a snow cone and an ice-cream cone alike and different? _____

    _____

14. How are a beehive and an anthill alike and different? _____

    _____

15. How are lakes and oceans alike and different? _____

    _____

16. How are radios and TVs alike and different? _____

    _____

17. How are the moon and stars alike and different? _____

    _____

18. How are zebras and horses alike and different? _____

    _____

19. How are kindergarten and preschool alike and different? _____

    _____

20. How are a swimming pool and a pond alike and different? _____

    _____

21. How are a Ferris wheel and a merry-go-round alike and different? _____

    _____

22. How are a telescope and binoculars alike and different? _____

    _____

23. How are a guitar and a violin alike and different? _____

    _____

24. How are a map and a globe alike and different? _____

    _____

I.E.P. Objective: The client will identify similarities and differences of objects/places/events with 90% or greater accuracy.

Task H: Identifying Similarities and Differences of Objects/Places/Events, *continued*

Answer each question stating one likeness and one difference for each pair of items.

25. How are a baseball cap and a cowboy hat alike and different? _____

_____

26. How are scissors and pliers alike and different? _____

_____

27. How are a hospital and a school alike and different? _____

_____

28. How are a parachute and an umbrella alike and different? _____

_____

29. How are walkie-talkies and telephones alike and different? _____

_____

30. How are newspapers and magazines alike and different? _____

_____

31. How are paperclips and staples alike and different? _____

_____

32. How are a wing and an arm alike and different? _____

_____

33. How are a dictionary and an encyclopedia alike and different? _____

_____

34. How are dragons and din█████ alike and different? _____

_____

35. How are Spiderman and Superman alike and different? _____

_____

36. How are a dream and a movie alike and different? _____

_____

I.E.P. Objective: *The client will identify similarities and differences of objects/places/events with 90% or greater*
accuracy.

Task I: Identifying Objects/Places/Actions from Descriptions

State the word for each definition. The first one is done for you.

1. a bath in which water sprays down from above _____*shower*_____

2. two babies born on the same day to the same parents _____

3. to open your mouth and breathe in deeply, especially when tired _____

4. to move from side to side, like a dog's tail _____

5. fast-food potato strips _____

6. bread that is made crisp and brown by heat _____

7. the hard outer covering of a turtle _____

8. a short oral or written test _____

9. a piece of cloth tied around a baby's neck during mealtime _____

10. to remove dirt by brushing with a broom _____

11. a long, slender piece of wood or metal used for hanging a flag _____

12. a drink made by squeezing oranges or apples _____

13. alert; not asleep _____

14. an area of land where cows graze _____

15. a color formed by combining blue and yellow _____

16. a form of matter that is not a solid or a gas _____

17. a container (or building) used for saving money _____

18. the child of your uncle or aunt _____

19. a head covering or the part of a car covering the engine _____

20. a paved walking path alongside a street _____

21. to swirl with a spoon _____

I.E.P. Objective: The client will identify objects/places/actions from descriptions with 90% or greater accuracy.

Task I: Identifying Objects/Places/Actions from Descriptions, *continued*

State the word for each definition.

22. an unsliced mound of bread   _____

23. a chart for keeping track of days and months   _____

24. a hard head covering that a soldier or bicyclist wears   _____

25. a bed covering made from blocks of bright fabric   _____

26. a sign above a door that shows where to go out   _____

27. a drawing of a country or state found in an atlas   _____

28. a shallow pool of water formed by rain   _____

29. a weighing instrument   _____

30. a shelter or repair shop for cars   _____

31. to name the letters of a word in the correct order   _____

32. the joint between the foot and the leg   _____

33. a cloth pouch sewn in or on clothing   _____

34. a ceremony when students receive diplomas   _____

35. a device for controlling the TV from a distance   _____

36. an animal that is hunted by another animal for food   _____

37. a mark left on the skin after a wound has healed   _____

38. to pay for something with a credit card rather than cash   _____

39. a person who rides a horse in a professional race   _____

40. a tube with loose bits of colored glass and mirrors at one
    end that shows different patterns as you turn it   _____

41. a series of movements done to stretch and strengthen the body _____

I.E.P. Objective: The client will identify objects/places/actions from descriptions with 90% or greater accuracy.

Describing Objects and Defining Words
Task J: Classifying Objects in Two or More Categories

Name two categories for each object. The first one is done for you.

1. apple _____*red things, fruit*_____

2. horse _____

3. pencil _____

4. stuffed animal _____

5. suitcase _____

6. airplane _____

7. boot _____

8. fish _____

9. pinwheel _____

10. motorcycle _____

11. nail _____

12. chewing gum _____

13. popcorn _____

14. book _____

15. pillow _____

16. snowflake _____

17. owl _____

18. dollar bill _____

19. telephone _____

20. ice cream _____

21. cave _____

I.E.P. Objective: The student will classify objects in two or more categories with 90% or greater accuracy.

Task J: Classifying Objects in Two or More Categories, *continued*

Name two categories for each object.

22. key _____

23. baseball cap _____

24. ice cube _____

25. purse _____

26. chalk _____

27. Swiss cheese _____

28. cough syrup _____

29. tractor _____

30. moss _____

31. raincoat _____

32. wallet _____

33. picture frame _____

34. dice _____

35. tea kettle _____

36. mattress _____

37. drinking straw _____

38. stilts _____

39. barrel _____

40. gasoline _____

41. starfish _____

42. poison ivy _____

I.E.P. Objective: The student will classify objects in two or more categories with 90% or greater accuracy.

Describing Objects and Defining Words
Task K: Completing Analogous Statements

Finish each statement with an appropriate word. The first one is done for you.

1. Cotton is soft. Stones are _____*hard*_____.

2. Chickens cluck. Pigs _____.

3. During the day we're awake. At night we're _____.

4. Fish have scales. Birds have _____.

5. A lawn mower cuts. A pen _____.

6. A brother is a boy. A sister is a _____.

7. Jackets are for winter. Shorts are for _____.

8. An oven heats. An air conditioner _____.

9. Bones are for dogs. Pacifiers are for _____.

10. People have hands. Cats have _____.

11. A cub is a baby bear. A calf is a baby _____.

12. Chickens come from eggs. Flowers come from _____.

13. Arms have elbows. Legs have _____.

14. A doe is a female deer. A hen is a female _____.

15. Sauce is for pasta. Milk is for _____.

16. Gum is for chewing. Lollipops are for _____.

17. CD cases are square. CDs are _____.

18. A deck is made of wood. A chimney is made of _____.

19. Water is a liquid. Ice is a _____.

20. November has Thanksgiving. February has _____.

21. A museum has paintings. A library has _____.

I.E.P. Objective: The client will complete analogous statements with 90% accuracy.

HELP for Language   62   Copyright © 2004 LinguiSystems, Inc.

Describing Objects and Defining Words
Task K: Completing Analogous Statements, *continued*

Finish each statement with an appropriate word.

22. Cupcakes have icing. Beds have _____.

23. Pianos have keys. Violins have _____.

24. Soccer players score goals. Baseball players score _____.

25. Apples have skins. Pecans have _____.

26. Seven is an odd number. Twelve is an _____ number.

27. Ballet dancers need shoes. Musicians need _____.

28. A clock has numerals. A stop sign has _____.

29. Envelopes hold letters. Wallets hold _____.

30. Doves coo. Owls _____.

31. Penguins waddle. Snakes _____.

32. Corn grows on a stalk. Grapes grow on a _____.

33. Bread goes stale. Milk goes _____.

34. Teachers give detentions. Police officers give _____.

35. A nail goes in a plank. A thumbtack goes in a _____.

36. Birds build nests. Beavers build _____.

37. Office workers have coffee breaks. School children have _____.

38. Your brain is in your skull. Your lungs are in your _____.

39. The leader of the U.S. is the President. The leader of a U.S. state is the _____.

40. The Empire State Building is in New York City. The Eiffel Tower is in _____.

41. *Uni* means *one*. *Tri* means _____.

42. A landscape is a painting of an outdoor scene. A portrait is a painting of a _____.

I.E.P. Objective: The client will complete analogous statements with 90% accuracy.

Describing Objects and Defining Words
Task L: Completing Analogies

Think about how the first two words are related. Then complete the second word pair. The first one is done for you. (*Note: You may present these analogies as completion items: "Roof is to house as lid is to _____." To simplify, provide the relationship of the first two items: "A roof covers the top of a house. A lid covers the top of a _____.")*

1.   roof : house :: lid : _____*box*_____

2.   broccoli : green :: carrot : _____

3.   ring : finger :: bracelet : _____

4.   rabbit : hop :: fish : _____

5.   cry : sad :: laugh : _____

6.   ant : hill :: bee : _____

7.   syrup: pancakes :: icing : _____

8.   ride : bike :: read : _____

9.   drink : straw :: eat : _____

10.   hug : arms :: kiss : _____

11.   glasses : eyes :: hearing aids : _____

12.   ocean : dolphin :: desert : _____

13.   cockroach : insect :: parakeet : _____

14.   mountain : high :: valley : _____

15.   bathing suit : pool :: pajamas : _____

16.   goal : soccer :: touchdown : _____

17.   triangle : three :: square : _____

18.   wild : wolf :: tame : _____

19.   perfume : smell :: gum : _____

I.E.P. Objective: The client will complete analogies with 90% accuracy.

Describing Objects and Defining Words
Task L: Completing Analogies, *continued*

Think about how the first two words are related. Then complete the second word pair.

20. ice cream : cone :: lollipop : _____

21. screwdriver : screw :: hammer : _____

22. ribbon : bow :: rope : _____

23. strawberries : vine :: cherries : _____

24. fly : kite :: jump : _____

25. soldier : march :: ballerina : _____

26. enormous : elephant :: tiny : _____

27. horse : hoof :: dog : _____

28. corn : cob :: apple : _____

29. rye : bread :: glazed : _____

30. one : two :: first : _____

31. scale : weight :: thermometer : _____

32. aquarium: fish tank : automobile: _____

33. agree : yes :: disagree : _____

34. pump : heart :: blink : _____

35. waves : ocean :: rapids : _____

36. grass : yard : : asphalt : _____

37. America : American :: Japan : _____

38. President : United States :: Queen/King : _____

39. peninsula : Florida :: island : _____

40. Ethiopia : Africa :: Brazil : _____

I.E.P. Objective: The client will complete analogies with 90% accuracy.

Task M: Identifying Common Characteristics of Objects

Name two characteristics each pair of objects share. The first one is done for you.

1. banana, lemon   _yellow, fruit_____

2. crab, lobster _____

3. kitten, puppy _____

4. crow, bat _____

5. hippopotamus, elephant _____

6. ocean, lake _____

7. carrot, potato _____

8. bracelet, ring _____

9. bowling ball, marble _____

10. stroller, grocery cart _____

11. hockey stick, baseball bat _____

12. blanket, towel _____

13. jelly, syrup _____

14. airplane, helicopter _____

15. pencil, pen _____

16. postage stamp, sticker _____

17. yo-yo, balloon _____

18. jacket, sweater _____

19. chewing gum, taffy _____

20. organ, piano _____

21. cabbage, lettuce _____

I.E.P. Objective: The client will identify characteristics shared by two objects with 90% or greater accuracy.

Task M: Identifying Common Characteristics of Objects, *continued*

Name two characteristics each pair of objects share.

22. lawn mower, vacuum cleaner _____

23. bicycle, motorcycle _____

24. mustard, butter _____

25. snowboard, skateboard _____

26. alligator, crocodile _____

27. needle, pin _____

28. roller coaster, water slide _____

29. acorn, walnut _____

30. gymnasium, stadium _____

31. movie, play _____

32. oatmeal, soup _____

33. chalkboard, Etch-a-Sketch® _____

34. trampoline, diving board _____

35. hedge, fence _____

36. inner tube, tire _____

37. telephone book, dictionary _____

38. calculator, cordless phone _____

39. telescope, microscope _____

40. unicorn, dragon _____

41. woodpecker, electric drill _____

42. Lifesaver® candy, drinking straw _____

I.E.P. Objective: The client will identify characteristics shared by two objects with 90% or greater accuracy.

Describing Objects and Defining Words
Task N: Choosing Descriptive Words

Choose the best word to complete each passage. The first one is done for you.

1. The teddy bears are having a parade. They carry colorful balloons. They laugh as they skip through the town. The teddy bears are _____.

   (happy)   scary   mean

2. Sam can do 15 pull-ups. He is on the swimming team and plays basketball every day after school. Sam is _____.

   honest   athletic   handsome

3. Kim gets a ten-dollar allowance each week, even though she doesn't do any chores at home. If Kim leaves her toys on the floor, her mother picks them up. She can eat candy anytime she wants. Kim is _____.

   spoiled   unhappy   poor

4. There are gray clouds overhead. The rain is falling steadily. The sun is behind the clouds and the air is chilly. The day is _____.

   bright   sunny   dreary

5. These strawberries are ready to be picked. They are red and juicy. These strawberries are _____.

   tough   rotten   ripe

6. On rainy Saturday mornings I like to pull the covers over my head and go back to sleep. The sound of the rain on the roof and the warmth of the blankets make me feel _____.

   drowsy   alert   hungry

7. My costume is red with shiny brass buttons on the front. The hat is covered with red, white, and blue feathers. Even my boots have bells on them. My costume is _____.

   simple   fancy   ragged

8. Shelia always turns in her homework on time. After school she helps out in her grandpa's shop. At home she helps her mother care for her brothers and sisters. Shelia is _____.

   careless   silly   responsible

I.E.P. Objective: The client will listen to descriptive passages and choose corresponding adjectives with 90% or greater accuracy.

Task N: Choosing Descriptive Words, *continued*

Choose the best word to complete each passage.

9. Ted was first in line at the buffet. He piled his plate high with shrimp, leaving only a few in the serving bowl. Ted's behavior was _____.

    greedy   jolly   mannerly

10. Ron's bed is unmade. His jeans and socks are on the floor. The trash can is overflowing. Ron's room is _____.

    tidy   cheerful   messy

11. Lily's ring is made of platinum and gold. It has a large diamond in the center surrounded by ten small rubies. Lily's ring is _____.

    valuable   inexpensive   plain

12. Mrs. Stone always turns out the lights when she leaves a room. She clips grocery coupons to use at the store. She never throws away anything unless it is worn out or used up. Mrs. Stone is _____.

    talkative   stubborn   thrifty

13. I could hardly keep my eyes open during the movie. There was too much talking and not enough action. The movie seemed to drag on forever. I thought the movie was _____.

    exciting   boring   frightening

14. Rudy will not finish her dinner. She will not clear her plate off the table. She won't push in her chair when her brother tries to walk by. Rudy is acting _____.

    stubborn   cooperative   scared

15. Our kitten is full of energy. It loves to run and tumble across the floor. Our kitten is _____.

    cozy   frisky   lazy

16. Morris picked up the dog carefully and placed it on a blanket. He moved the dog's leg back and forth very slowly to see if it was broken. Then he softly patted the dog's head to calm him. Morris is _____.

    hysterical   gentle   gloomy

I.E.P. Objective: The client will listen to descriptive passages and choose corresponding adjectives with 90% or greater accuracy.

Task N: Choosing Descriptive Words, *continued*

Choose the best word to complete each passage.

17. Julie thought the show started at 4:00, but the parking lot was empty. When she tries the door of the theater, it is locked. Julie is _____.

      broke   exhausted   confused

18. I was trying to talk to Maria, but Shelly kept interrupting me. Each time she interrupted me, Shelly tapped me on the arm. Shelly's behavior was _____.

      awesome   annoying   scary

19. Mr. Ford got up at dawn and began building a brick wall around his backyard. He worked all morning without stopping. At one o'clock, his wife called him inside for lunch. Mr. Ford fell asleep on the couch before lunch was served. Mr. Ford was _____.

      wise   sloppy   weary

20. I set the VCR to record my favorite TV show while I was at the game. But when I rewound the tape and played it, nothing was on it. The tape was _____.

      blank   loud   uneven

21. Al stood up when his grandmother entered the room and offered her his chair. Al is _____.

      famous   hopeless   courteous

22. Joel's heart was beating fast and his palms were sweaty. When he peeked out from behind the curtain and saw how many people were in the audience, he felt a little dizzy. He hoped his name was not called next. Joel was _____.

      confident   nervous   relieved

23. Kaylen worked hard on her science project, but she didn't win a ribbon in the science fair. When Kaylen saw Tina's blue ribbon, she thought, "Her project isn't half as good as mine!" Kaylen is _____.

      proud   jealous   shy

24. Mom said, "We don't have time to look for your library book. Grab your shoes and you can put them on in the car. I'm leaving right now!" Mom is _____.

      impatient   hopeful   sorry

I.E.P. Objective: The client will listen to descriptive passages and choose corresponding adjectives with 90% or greater accuracy.

Task N: Choosing Descriptive Words, *continued*

Choose the best word to complete each passage.

25. When Mrs. Dixon knelt down to help the children do a puzzle, she heard a loud rip. When she felt the back of her pants, she realized the seam had split open. The children started giggling. Mrs. Dixon is _____.

                embarrassed   clumsy   excited

26. We woke up early and went outside. From where we stood, we could barely see the house across the street. The view is _____.

                gritty   sharp   hazy

27. After practicing for three weeks, Janet didn't get a part in the school play. Janet was _____.

                discouraged   pleased   elated

28. Ellen wants to be class president. She is campaigning hard. She has talked to each student and put up 50 posters around school. Ellen is _____.

                unable   evil   ambitious

29. When I couldn't find my new ring, Jessica said, "Don't worry. If we all search for it, we will find it. It will turn up somewhere." Jessica is _____.

                depressed   unconcerned   optimistic

30. Elijah won the race in the last lap. Elijah was _____.

                victorious   ordinary   bewildered

31. When Carlos was moving his computer monitor from the table to his desk, he dropped it on his foot. The next day he had to run cross-country for track. The pain in his foot was _____.

                comforting   agonizing   encouraging

32. According to Dr. Williams, the operation will take only one hour. She said I should be able to go home the next morning and go back to work in three days. She told me she has performed this type of operation over 500 times. Dr. Williams' remarks were _____.

                reassuring   entertaining   threatening

I.E.P. Objective: The client will listen to descriptive passages and choose corresponding adjectives with 90% or greater accuracy.

Task O: Identifying Word Meanings from Contextual Cues

Give the meaning of each bolded word. The first one is done for you.

1. It's your turn. See if you can **swat** the birdie over the net with your racket. _____*hit*_____

2. Ned was scared on the roller coaster. After the ride stopped, he still **clutched** the bar tightly with both hands. _____

3. Al got in the shower and jumped right back out. The water was **scalding** hot. _____

4. This ruler is very **flexible**. I can bend it in a circle and it doesn't break. _____

5. It's not a good day to surf. The ocean is so **calm** there are no waves. _____

6. I have one more **task** to do. Then I will be done with all the jobs on my list. _____

7. After the rain, the pond was **murky**. We couldn't see our toes when we waded in the water.

   _____

8. Joe is fascinated by **marine** life. He loves anything that has to do with the sea. _____

9. We have a **pantry** in our kitchen. Even though it is a small closet, we keep all our food, spices, and other kitchen supplies there. _____

10. The team doesn't have **funds** to buy new uniforms. They will try to raise the money by selling peanuts. _____

11. Uncle Ed loves to **whittle**. He sits on the porch with his knife and a block of wood and makes beautiful animals. _____

12. Mr. Shaw's car is **unique**. There are no others exactly like it. _____

13. The actors received a standing **ovation**. Everyone clapped and cheered loudly for them.

   _____

14. The forest is very **dense**. The trees are so close together you can hardly walk between them.

   _____

15. Doves sound **mournful**. When they coo it sounds as if they have lost their best friend.

   _____

16. I'm taking my sister to the park today as I promised. I cannot break another **pledge** to her.

   _____

I.E.P. Objective: The client will use contextual cues to identify word meanings with 90% or greater accuracy.

Give the meaning of each bolded word.

17. We grow some **exotic** plants in our greenhouse. Several of our orchids are from faraway countries. _____

18. Don't **jostle** my arm! I'm trying to glue this toy back together and I need to hold it steady.

_____

19. The microwave oven must be broken. I heated this water on high for five minutes and it is barely **lukewarm**. _____

20. Mom wouldn't give her **consent** for me to go on the school trip. She thinks I am too young to go so far from home without her. _____

21. Your English papers must have a 1½ inch **margin** on all sides. This provides space for me to write comments about your writing. _____

22. Playing tricks on people on the first of April is a **custom** in many countries. People trick their friends year after year. _____

23. Stan tried to **persuade** me to change my mind. He had some good points, but I'm still voting for Dan. _____

24. Click on the **icon** of the program you want to use. If you want to play solitaire, click on the playing cards. _____

25. The bear cub tumbled into a **ravine**. It was too deep for the cub to climb out and the sides were too steep for the mother bear to reach the cub. _____

26. I did not **comprehend** the last math problem. No matter how many times the teacher explained it, I still didn't understand it. _____

27. Dad is making me return the **midriff** top I just bought. He said I am not allowed to go to school with the middle part of my body showing. _____

28. You will rarely see a flying fox during the day. It is a **nocturnal** animal. _____

29. We were excited to find an **intact** sand dollar at the beach. In the past, every sand dollar we've found has been broken. _____

I.E.P. Objective: The client will use contextual cues to identify word meanings with 90% or greater accuracy.

73

Reading and Listening
Task A: Predicting Content from Titles

Use the title to choose the best content for each story.

1. *A Puppy for Paul*

    a. Paul wins a race
    b. Paul gets a new dog.
    c. Paul's dog runs away.

2. *Runaway Reindeer*

    a. An airplane misses the runway.
    b. Sarah runs away in the rain.
    c. Prancer leaves the North Pole.

3. *Nosey Nick*

    a. Nick spoils his sister's birthday party.
    b. Nick reads his sister's diary while she's at school.
    c. Nick's sister hits him in the nose with a fly ball.

4. *The New Kid in School*

    a. Harry rides the bus to school.
    b. Harry misses the school field trip.
    c. Harry is nervous about the first day of school.

5. *The Case of the Missing Key*

    a. A detective searches for a missing key.
    b. Ellie gets a new locket.
    c. A bank robber gets caught.

6. *Go for the Gold*

    a. Stan finds a five-dollar bill.
    b. Jeremy wins a first-place medal.
    c. Kate does not win the spelling bee.

7. *Midnight Munchies*

    a. Steven's father joins him at school for lunch.
    b. At nightfall, the daylilies turn into fairies.
    c. Deer eat all the lettuce in the garden overnight.

8. *Slam Dunk*

    a. Eva wrecks her new car.
    b. Eva scores the winning basket.
    c. Eva eats doughnuts and coffee.

I.E.P. Objective: The client will predict content from story titles with 90% or greater accuracy.

Task A: Predicting Content from Titles, *continued*

Use the title to choose the best content for each story.

9. *Doorway to Disaster*

    a. Pat steps into the elevator and smells smoke.
    b. Pat opens the closet and her cat runs out.
    c. Pat steps through the door and her friends yell, "Surprise!"

10. *Silent Night*

    a. Eight friends have a sleepover.
    b. Lincoln High wins the state football championship.
    c. A winter storm downs the telephone and power lines.

11. *A Year to Remember*

    a. Martin's baseball team wins five games and loses five.
    b. Cindy competes on the U.S. Olympic Diving Team.
    c. The Perini family trades in their old car for a new one.

12. *The Secret of King's Creek*

    a. A treasure is found buried in the desert.
    b. A safe is found at the bottom of the ocean.
    c. Children wading in a creek find a map in a bottle.

13. *Our Prairie Home*

    a. Pioneers travel west and settle in Kansas.
    b. Miners find gold in California.
    c. Colonists settle in Jamestown.

14. *We All Fall Down*

    a. The baseball team practices batting.
    b. The Carr family takes skiing lessons.
    c. A gaggle of geese fly south in autumn.

15. *A Visit from Lady Luck*

    a. Stanley's aunt visits from Ireland.
    b. Stanley's dog, Lady, has puppies.
    c. Stanley buys a winning lottery ticket.

16. *Let the Truth Be Told*

    a. Mr. Tyler takes the witness stand.
    b. Mr. Tyler gives a campaign speech.
    c. Mr. Tyler describes the fish he almost caught.

I.E.P. Objective: The client will predict content from story titles with 90% or greater accuracy.

Task A: Predicting Content from Titles, *continued*

Use the title to choose the content for each story.

17. *Chill Out*

> a. Rob goes in the penalty box during an ice hockey game.
> b. Rob hits a fly and it is caught by an outfielder.
> c. Rob gets bad news in the mail.

18. *White Sails, Blue Sea*

> a. Katie goes scuba diving on the Great Barrier Reef.
> b. Katie learns to water ski on Lake Okeechobee.
> c. Katie rides on a schooner sailing from Boston Harbor.

19. *Trek to the Top*

> a. Four climbers ascend Mt. McKinley.
> b. 1,000 Star Trek fans attend a convention.
> c. Jackie wins three gold medals in track and field.

20. *Rush Hour*

> a. Some friends bake cookies.
> b. Some friends go whitewater rafting.
> c. Some friends look at vacation photos.

21. *Starstruck*

> a. A meteorite hits the barn.
> b. Alicia meets her favorite movie star.
> c. A careless driver hits the back of Alvin's truck.

22. *A Precious Gift*

> a. France gives the Statue of Liberty to the United States.
> b. Evan buys his dog a new collar.
> c. Mr. Reynolds gets a free umbrella when he renews his newspaper subscription.

23. *The Wright Flight*

> a. Mrs. Strauss misses her flight to Boston.
> b. Jacob wins a kite-flying contest.
> c. The Wright brothers made the first successful flight in a real aircraft.

24. *Technicolor Dreams*

> a. Thomas King studies to become a movie director.
> b. June Wells studies to become a country music star.
> c. Marshall Kelly dreams of becoming an astronaut.

I.E.P. Objective: The client will predict content from story titles with 90% or greater accuracy.

76

Reading and Listening
Task B: Identifying the Main Idea

Listen to (or read) each paragraph. Then choose the main idea.

1. A pocketknife is useful when camping. You might need it to cut a rope when setting up your campsite. If you are missing a tent stake, you can use your knife to make one from a stick. When you go fishing, a pocketknife is helpful for cutting bait and fishing lines. If you use your knife to sharpen one end of a long stick, you can cook hot dogs or marshmallows over the campfire.

   a. It is difficult to set up a campsite.
   b. A pocketknife is a helpful tool when camping.
   c. Children shouldn't play with knives.

2. Pets depend on their owners for many things. Pet owners must give their pets food, water, and shelter. Some pets, such as dogs, need attention from their owners every day. Pet owners must be careful so their pets do not run away or get injured. When a pet is ill or injured, its owner must take the pet to the vet.

   a. Dogs make the best pets.
   b. Children cannot be responsible for taking care of pets.
   c. Pet owners have a lot of responsibility.

3. Grocery shopping is not an easy chore. There are so many different brands and types of food that it can be hard to make a choice. Do we want smooth peanut butter or chunky, regular or low fat, plain or swirled with grape jelly, large or small container, glass or plastic jar? And which brand do we prefer? With so many choices for each item, no wonder it takes so long to shop!

   a. More people buy smooth peanut butter than chunky.
   b. You must make many decisions when buying groceries.
   c. If you want to shop quickly, don't buy peanut butter.

4. Extreme sports are very popular. Some extreme sports, such as snow skiing or surfing, have been around for many years. Other extreme sports, such as snowboarding or windsurfing, have become popular in recent years. One thing all extreme sports have in common is the thrill of competing. Extreme sports athletes are always looking for new challenges — a bigger wave, a higher mountain, or a steeper hill.

   a. Extreme sports are dangerous.
   b. Extreme sports are new.
   c. Many people are interested in extreme sports.

I.E.P. Objective: The client will identify the main idea of paragraphs with 90% or greater accuracy.

Task B: Identifying the Main Idea, *continued*

Listen to (or read) each paragraph. Then choose the main idea.

5. Auto race officials use flags to signal the drivers. A green flag means go and a red flag means stop. The official waves a red flag when an accident or bad weather has made the track dangerous. When drivers see a yellow flag, they must slow down and keep from passing others. The official uses a white flag to signal the last lap of the race. The familiar black and white checkered flag means the race is over.

    a. Officials use colored flags to communicate with drivers during an auto race.
    b. Racecar drivers may pass on a yellow flag during the last lap of the race.
    c. Racecar drivers wave red flags if they need to make an emergency stop.

6. Many years ago, libraries were silent places offering mostly books and newspapers. Today, we can find a variety of resources in libraries. In addition to regular books, libraries loan out books-on-tape, videotapes, and compact disks. Most libraries have replaced their card catalogs with computer catalogs. Shelves of current magazines and comfortable chairs encourage people to relax and stay a while. Children are welcomed to the library with brightly-colored murals, puzzle tables, and story hours.

    a. Public libraries have changed slightly over the years.
    b. Computer catalogs make it easier to find books.
    c. Libraries have become more user-friendly.

7. The people who live in Africa speak more different languages than on any other continent. There are 800 ethnic groups in Africa, each with its own language. Some groups even have more than one language. There are over 1,000 different languages in all. In some places, Africans speak popular languages such as Arabic, Portuguese, French, and English. In other areas in Africa, the people may speak several different languages within the same country. Somalia is the only country in Africa where everyone speaks the same language.

    a. Africa is a continent of many people and many languages.
    b. No one in Africa speaks the same language.
    c. The most popular language in Africa is Arabic.

I.E.P. Objective: The client will identify the main idea of paragraphs with 90% or greater accuracy.

Task B: Identifying the Main Idea, *continued*

Listen to (or read) each paragraph. Then choose the main idea.

8. Koala bears aren't really bears. They are marsupials. Kangaroos are also marsupials. Koala bears carry their babies in a pouch, just like kangaroos. Unlike kangaroos, koala bears spend most of their time in trees. The only reason they come down from the trees is to find food. They like to eat eucalyptus leaves.

    a. Kangaroos and koala bears are enemies.

    b. Koala bears are marsupials that eat leaves.

    c. Koala bears are too heavy to climb trees.

9. There are many different types of instruments. Violins and guitars are stringed instruments. Musicians move the strings on these instruments to play them. To play pianos and organs, you press the keys on their keyboards. To play wind instruments, such as a horn or a flute, you blow into them while pressing keys. Musicians play drums, cymbals, and other percussion instruments by striking them.

    a. Instruments are played in different ways.

    b. Instruments made of brass are the loudest.

    c. If you hit a percussion instrument, it will crack.

10. If asked which animal eats leaves from the treetops, you might think of a giraffe. Would you also think of sauropods? These dinosaurs had very long necks that helped them reach vegetation high off the ground. Their long necks may also have helped them reach plants in lakebeds. Sauropods must have spent much of their days eating in order to take in enough food to fuel their enormous bodies.

    a. Sauropods were vegetarians with long necks.

    b. Sauropods died because they could not eat enough leaves.

    c. Giraffes are related to dinosaurs.

11. Nourishing food is only one benefit of the family dinner hour. Studies show that when families eat together, children earn better grades and are less likely to have high levels of stress. Parents can teach manners, family values, and vocabulary at the dinner table. The family dinner hour is also a good time to talk about what happened in each person's day and plan for the next day.

    a. Good nutrition leads to good grades.

    b. When parents work late, children are not nourished.

    c. Gathering around the table for dinner has many benefits.

I.E.P. Objective: The client will identify the main idea of paragraphs with 90% or greater accuracy.

Listen to (or read) each paragraph. Then choose the main idea.

12. A dollar bill is an object we use almost every day, yet most people probably know little about it. This paper money isn't actually made of paper at all. It is made of a blend of cotton and linen fibers, which is why it holds up so well when it goes through the washer and dryer in our pockets. After a bill is printed with a special secret ink, it is starched to make it crisp and waterproof. A typical dollar bill is in circulation for about 18 months. Compare this to the nine-year lifespan of a one hundred dollar bill and you will see how much wear and tear a one dollar bill receives.

   a. One dollar bills are stronger than one hundred dollar bills.

   b. One dollar bills are used often and wear out quickly.

   c. A one dollar bill expires 18 months after it is printed.

13. What starts out as an egg the size of a pinhead and ends up a colorful beauty? If you guessed *butterfly*, you are right! A newly-hatched caterpillar is very hungry and loves fresh milkweed. As it grows, it sheds its skin four or five times. When it hangs upside down and turns green, it is forming its chrysalis. In several weeks, the chrysalis turns gray and then transparent. Soon the butterfly emerges. After the powdery scales on its wings dry, the butterfly takes its first flight. What a beautiful sight!

   a. Milkweed is a butterfly's favorite food.

   b. Moths and butterflies go through the same stages.

   c. There are many stages in a butterfly's life.

14. Although most people no longer carry handkerchiefs or bandanas, they can come in handy. Cowboys used their bandanas to keep dust out of their noses and mouths, tie their hats on in strong winds, keep the sun from burning their necks, and strain dirt from drinking water. Campers use bandanas as emergency slings or bandages; as tiebacks for their hair when cooking over a campfire; and as dishrags, washcloths, or napkins. With so many uses, it's a wonder that people stopped carrying handkerchiefs.

   a. Cowboys and campers have little in common.

   b. People stopped carrying handkerchiefs because they are no longer sold in stores.

   c. Handkerchiefs are very functional.

I.E.P. Objective: The client will identify the main idea of paragraphs with 90% or greater accuracy.

HELP for Language   80

Task B: Identifying the Main Idea, *continued*

Listen to (or read) each paragraph. Then choose the main idea.

15. In 1870, people began to commonly use bicycles in the United States. Early bikes had huge front wheels and small back wheels. They were very hard to pedal. By the turn of the 20th century, two-wheelers looked much like the bikes we ride today. In the 1960s, ten-speed racers rolled into our lives. The 1970s brought banana seats and high handlebars. Today, high-tech mountain bikes are lightweight, yet rugged.

    a. Bicycles have become more expensive.

    b. Bicycles have undergone many changes over the years.

    c. Bicycles are the most common form of transportation.

16. Many people find it hard to wake up in the morning. We groan and reach for the snooze button when the alarm goes off. Busy days and late nights make it hard to get enough sleep. Even when we do get to bed on time, unfinished business from the day or worries about tomorrow's events can keep us from falling asleep. Our ancestors would laugh at the thought of being unable to fall asleep. After toiling in the fields or factories from early morning until evening, they had no problem falling asleep. But they, too, probably groaned at the sound of the rooster crowing early in the morning.

    a. Many people have difficulty falling asleep and waking up in the morning.

    b. If we worked harder, it would be easier to wake up in the morning.

    c. Before the invention of alarm clocks, many people overslept and were late for their jobs.

17. The Internet has become a quick and easy way to find information on just about any topic. When using the Internet to do research, however, you must be careful of the source. Just because someone has posted information on a website, it doesn't mean the person is an expert. Anyone can offer his opinion as fact on the Internet. Official websites of the government, newspapers, colleges, and professional organizations may have more reliable information than other sites. If you compare several sites and find the same facts, you can be more confident the information is correct.

    a. Most people lie when posting information on the Internet.

    b. Not all information on the Internet is reliable.

    c. All information on the Internet has been verified as true.

I.E.P. Objective: The client will identify the main idea of paragraphs with 90% or greater accuracy.

        81

Task C: Paraphrasing Passages

Listen to each passage. Then retell it in your own words. Be sure to include at least three important details. (*Note: You may choose to break up a paragraph into smaller parts as you read it.*)

1. Some of the best children's games aren't played on an electronic game system. For hundreds of years, children have entertained themselves with tag, hide-and-go-seek, races, and jump rope. Young children always enjoy ring-around-the-rosy, and older children love hopscotch and kick-the-can. Children have taught us that we can find fun beyond expensive packages.

2. When bowling, it's important to choose a ball that fits your fingers. If the holes are too snug, you won't be able to release the ball easily. If the holes are too large, the ball may slip out of your hand before you are ready. The weight of the ball is important too. You need to be able to pick up and roll the ball easily, yet you want a ball that's heavy enough to knock down the pins with force.

3. Everyone should learn how to swim, especially people who live near the water. It is important to learn how to hold your breath, go under the water, and come back up. You should also be able to float for at least five minutes so you can stay afloat in an emergency. Jump into a pool with your clothes on to practice staying afloat with the added weight of wet clothing. Some-day you could save your own life using basic water survival skills.

4. Why are hyenas called *laughing hyenas*? In movies and cartoons, hyenas laugh just like people. A real hyena doesn't laugh exactly like a human, although its call may sound like wild laughter. Hyenas make other noises, too, such as howling, snarling, and barking. Hyenas are nocturnal animals. If you hear strange laughing outdoors at night, it just might be a hyena!

5. How could you time something if you had no watch? Many years ago people used hourglasses. An hourglass measures time by the trickling of sand or water through a small opening at the bottom of a glass bulb. The sand or water moves through the narrow opening into a glass bulb below. When the top bulb is empty, one hour has passed. Today we use smaller timers to keep track of minutes when we play a game or cook an egg.

6. Clothing is made from different materials. These materials come from plants or animals, or they are made from chemicals. Much of our clothing is made from cotton, which comes from a plant. Linen is another cloth that comes from a plant. Wool comes from a sheep or a goat. Leather for shoes, coats, and belts comes from a cow. Some cloth, such as polyester or nylon, is made from chemicals.

I.E.P. Objective: The client will paraphrase informational passages with 90% or greater accuracy.

Listen to each passage. Then retell it in your own words. Be sure to include at least three important details.

7. You may shout "punch buggy," "slug bug," or "bug alert" when you see a small car with a rounded shape, but its proper name is Volkswagen. The first Volkswagens were built in Germany in the 1930s. The manufacturers wanted to build a car that was inexpensive and easy to fix. They wanted a car that almost everyone could buy and enjoy. So, that's what they called it. In German, the word *Volks* means *people* and *Wagen* means *car*. When you put these words together, *Volkswagen* means *people's car*. The next time you see one, yell, "People's car!"

8. We can recycle many common objects. Newspapers, magazines, cardboard, milk cartons, plastic containers, and glass bottles are all recyclable. Some communities have curbside pickup to make recycling easier for residents. Other communities have drop-off sites where people can leave their items. We can also support recycling by buying goods made from recycled items. Lawn furniture, computer paper, cereal boxes, and mulch are just some of the new goods made from recycled items.

9. Do you know the most popular sport in the world? If you live in the United States, you might think it is baseball. But it isn't! Hundreds of millions of people worldwide play soccer, making it the most popular sport of all. In most countries, people call this game *football*. The world's largest soccer tournament, the World Cup, takes place every four years. Each country's best players compete for the World Cup. Since 1991, both men's and women's teams play in this tournament. The U.S. men's team has never won the World Cup, but the U.S. women's team won in 1991 and 1999.

10. What happens if you press your forehead against a cool glass mirror? The glass feels warmer and your skin feels cooler. That's because energy or heat flowed from your warm forehead to the cooler glass of the mirror. Heat usually flows from warmer to cooler materials. If you pick up something cool, the heat from your hand will warm it. If you pick up something hot, it will warm your cooler hand. Think about this the next time you warm your hands around a cup of hot chocolate or shiver when you grab the metal railing while ice skating.

I.E.P. Objective: The client will paraphrase informational passages with 90% or greater accuracy.

Task C: Paraphrasing Passages, *continued*

Listen to each passage. Then retell it in your own words. Be sure to include at least three important details.

11. Have you ever seen a horse wearing blinders? These dark shades rest alongside a horse's head so it can't see to either side. While wearing blinders, the horse must focus on what is in front of it. This keeps the horse from being frightened by something unexpected coming up behind it. Horse owners use blinders on racehorses and on workhorses pulling wagons or carts. Blinders help horses concentrate on their work and reduce the chance that a horse might become scared and bolt, injuring itself or others.

12. Puffins are unusual looking birds with bright orange beaks and black-and-white feathers. People have nicknamed them *sea parrot* or *ocean clown*. They use their big beaks to carry fish. They are excellent swimmers and can stay underwater for up to one minute. Puffins live in both the Atlantic and Pacific oceans. They build their nests under big rocks on islands and lay only one egg each year. A baby puffin is called a puffling. When a puffin is six weeks old, it flies out to the ocean where it lives for the next few years. At five years of age, the puffin returns to the place it was hatched to breed and raise pufflings of its own.

13. Reference books contain a wealth of information, but they will be of little help unless you use the correct one. If you are trying to locate a certain place, use an atlas, which is a book of maps. A dictionary is the best source for definitions, spellings, and pronunciations of words. If you want to find only synonyms of words, look in a thesaurus. If you need to find detailed information about a person, place, or historical event, use an encyclopedia. When traveling, use guidebooks for information and directions.

14. A new source of toxic trash is discarded cell phones. When people switch to new wireless phone carriers, they often throw away their old phones. Millions of discarded cell phones end up in landfills where they can leak chemicals into the groundwater. When we burn cell phones in incinerators, they leak toxins that pollute the air. Even though wireless phone companies collect old phones at their stores for recycling, this is not enough to handle the millions of phones that people discard each year. Most consumers don't know that wireless telephones can be recycled. Public awareness must be raised about programs to recycle used phones so that consumers can help reduce this growing mountain of trash.

I.E.P. Objective: The client will paraphrase informational passages with 90% or greater accuracy.

Task D: Answering Interpretive Questions from Stories

Listen to (or read) each story. Then answer the questions.

1. Dylan held his breath and tried not to move a muscle. He could feel his heart beating rapidly. The footsteps were getting closer and closer. Suddenly they stopped. From his leafy perch, Dylan could see only the legs and feet of the person who was chasing him. Dylan couldn't remain still any longer. As he shifted his weight, his shoe fell to the ground. Immediately, Dylan was caught in the beam of a flashlight. "Your goose is cooked!" screamed Marie. "Now you are it!"

    a. Why was Dylan holding his breath?

    b. Where was Dylan hiding?

    c. What details in the story give you a hint about Dylan's hiding place?

    d. What time of day did the story take place?

    e. Why did Dylan's shoe fall off?

    f. Did Dylan get hurt when he was caught in the flashlight's beam?

    g. What did Marie mean when she said, "Your goose is cooked!"?

    h. What game were Marie and Dylan playing?

    i. How does the feeling of the story change from the beginning to the end?

    j. What is a good title for this story?

2. "But Mom," said Kyle. "All the other kids are allowed to ride their bikes around the block. You treat me like such a baby!"

    "Well, it seems like just yesterday that you were a baby riding your tricycle," answered Kyle's mom. "You may ride your bike around the block one time. Look out for cars. Stay near the side of the road. Don't forget to wear your gear!"

    Several minutes after Kyle left, his mother heard the squeal of tires and the screech of brakes. Her heart was in her throat. She ran out the front door and saw Kyle riding toward her very fast. As he jumped off his bike and ran toward her, Kyle yelled, "Mom, Mr. Byrd almost got hit by a car when he backed out of his driveway! He wasn't being careful like me!" Kyle's mom smiled and hugged him tightly.

    a. How old do you think Kyle is, and what details in the story give you a hint about his age?

    b. Has Kyle ridden his bike around the block before today?

I.E.P. Objective: The client will answer interpretive questions from short stories with 90% or greater accuracy.

85

    c. What word describes Kyle's feeling about his ability to ride his bike around the block by himself?

    d. How does Kyle's mom feel about him going around the block?

    e. What did Kyle's mom mean when she told him to wear his gear?

    f. What did Kyle's mom think had happened when she heard the screech of brakes?

    g. What is the meaning of the statement, "Her heart was in her throat"?

    h. How do you think Kyle's mom felt when she saw him riding toward her?

    i. Why did Kyle's mom smile as she hugged him?

    j. What is a good title for this story?

3. Clayton was burning the midnight oil studying for tomorrow's algebra final. At 1:00 AM, Clayton still had 15 pages to review. But he could no longer keep his eyes open, so he hit the sack. All night Clayton dreamed of numbers and equations. The numbers were after him, trying to invade his house and surround him. Clayton could even hear the numbers hitting the glass of his bedroom windows, ping, ping, pinging as they tried to get inside. Clayton huddled deeper under the blankets, covering his ears, but still the sound of the numbers hitting the glass kept him from sleeping soundly.

Finally it was morning. Clayton shut off the alarm and stumbled from bed, dreading to face the day. Then he glanced out the window and saw the ground blanketed in white. Clayton hurriedly turned on the radio, hoping and praying to hear Heritage High on the list.

    a. What does the phrase "burning the midnight oil" mean, and why was Clayton doing it?

    b. Did Clayton finish studying for his exam before he went to bed?

    c. Why do you think Clayton was dreaming about numbers and equations?

    d. What was actually making the pinging sound on his windows?

    e. Why was Clayton dreading the day ahead?

    f. How do you think Clayton felt when he looked out the window?

    g. Why did Clayton turn on the radio?

    h. Why was Clayton hoping to hear Heritage High on the list?

    i. How old do you think Clayton is, and what details in the story give you a clue about his age?

    j. What is a good title for this story?

I.E.P. Objective: The client will answer interpretive questions from short stories with 90% or greater accuracy.

Task D: Answering Interpretive Questions from Stories, *continued*

4. As Billy closed the barn door, he heard screams coming from the direction of the river. He jumped on his horse and galloped eastward. As he approached the river, he could see several people gathered on its bank near an overturned wagon. Two people stretched out a long limb into the swift current. "Swim, Carol, swim!" screamed Mrs. Olson.

   Billy jumped off his horse, pulled off his boots, and plunged into the river. Kicking and pulling hard, he reached Carol quickly. He grabbed onto the long skirt of her dress and pulled her toward the branch, grabbing it and holding fast. The others pulled the branch to the bank, and Billy and Carol were safe.

   "My baby, you saved my baby!" cried Mrs. Olson. "How will I ever repay you?"

   "It was nothing, ma'am," replied Billy.

   "Cut!" yelled Jack. "Brad and Courtney, get dried off for another take. And this time Courtney, go under the water a few times before he reaches you."

   a. Where and when might this story have taken place?
   b. Did Billy know what the problem was before he jumped on his horse?
   c. Why were people stretching a limb into the river?
   d. What is a possible reason why no one jumped into the river before Billy arrived?
   e. Why did Billy take off his boots before jumping into the river?
   f. Why was Carol wearing a long dress in the river?
   g. How are Mrs. Olson and Carol related?
   h. Who are Jack, Brad, and Courtney?
   i. At what point did you realize the story was a scene from a movie?
   j. What is a good title for this story?

5. George felt the ladder wobble as he shifted his weight. Suddenly the ladder began to fall. George dropped his brush and grabbed for the rain gutter as the ladder crashed down onto the orange tree in the backyard. Luckily George was able to grab the gutter with both hands. He tried to inch his way down the gutter toward a tree that leaned close to the house, but each time he moved, the gutter pulled farther away from the house.

   George hung there, suspended above the yard like a clumsy tightrope walker, unable to move and unwilling to jump three stories to the ground. "Why

I.E.P. Objective: The client will answer interpretive questions from short stories with 90% or greater accuracy.

Task D: Answering Interpretive Questions from Stories, *continued*

couldn't this have happened yesterday when I was painting the front of the house?" thought George. "But, in my twenty years on the job, I've been in worse jams than this. I'll figure some way out of this one too!" Just then he heard a little boy's voice below.

"Whatcha doing up there, Mister?" he asked.

   a. What is George's job, and how do you know this?

   b. Where could this story have taken place, and what details in the story give you a hint about the setting?

   c. What detail in the story gives you information about George's age, and how old do you think he is?

   d. Why is George trying to inch his way down the gutter toward a tree?

   e. Why is George unwilling to jump to the ground?

   f. How is George like a clumsy tightrope walker?

   g. Why does George wish the ladder had fallen yesterday?

   h. How would you describe George's attitude as he hangs from the gutter?

   i. How do you think George will get out of this jam?

   j. What is a good title for this story?

6. Renee gazed out the window. She could just make out the lights of Richmond through the clouds. "Hurry up!" she cheered silently. "I've waited three long years for this trip. I can't wait another minute." Soon enough Renee found herself at the baggage claim area. She grabbed her suitcase from the carousel and ran toward the door where she saw Sue waiting with outstretched arms. As Sue hugged Renee, she said, "Come on. Mom is waiting in the car with my special guy. I can't wait for you to meet him!"

As Renee and Sue hurried to the car, Renee saw a man following her. He looked suspicious, wearing dark glasses and a dark coat. "Quick, let's get in the car," said Renee. As they drove off, Renee glanced out the back window of the car. The man was running after her. She was glad she was in the car.

Renee then turned her attention to Danny who grinned at her excitedly. "I'm your Aunt Renee," she said. "And you are even cuter than your pictures. I brought you a surprise. Let me open my suitcase and get it." But when Renee opened her suitcase, she was the one who was surprised. Instead of a rubber duckie and a stuffed bunny, she found a man's jacket and a box of business cards.

I.E.P. Objective: The client will answer interpretive questions from short stories with 90% or greater accuracy.

Task D: Answering Interpretive Questions from Stories, *continued*

     a. How was Renee traveling, and how do you know this?

     b. How are Sue and Renee related?

     c. Who is Sue's special guy?

     d. Why hasn't Renee met Danny before today?

     e. What about the man made Renee suspicious?

     f. What was Renee expecting to see when she opened her suitcase?

     g. Why was the man following Renee in the airport?

     h. What could Renee have done to avoid this problem?

     i. How do you think Renee will get the suitcase to its owner?

     j. What would be a good title for this story?

7. "I knew he couldn't be trusted!" yelled Shannon as she yanked the cash box from the drawer. "Just look. There were five one-hundred dollar bills in here yesterday. Now there are just two. Richard closed up last night. He must have taken the money!"

Janet straightened the last necktie in the display case and stood up. "Calm down, Shannon," she cautioned. "Although Richard hasn't worked here long, he seems very honest. Last week he ran after a woman to give her a nickel in change. Does that sound like a dishonest person?"

"That was just a smokescreen. His shift was supposed to start at 9:00 and it's already 9:30. If he didn't take the money, why isn't he here yet? I'll bet we won't be seeing any more of him!" snapped Shannon.

"Ask him yourself!" retorted Janet as the bell on the front door jangled and Richard came in.

"Good morning, everyone!" said Richard. "Sorry I'm a little late. There was a long line at the bank, but I got the change you asked me to get. The twenties are in this envelope and here are the coins. And I also stopped and got some bagels for everyone. Help yourself!"

     a. Where and when does this story take place?

     b. What does Shannon mean when she says that Richard closed up last night?

     c. Why wouldn't a dishonest person run after someone to give her a nickel?

     d. What did Shannon mean when she said, "That was just a smokescreen"?

I.E.P. Objective: The client will answer interpretive questions from short stories with 90% or greater accuracy.

    e. Why does Shannon think that Richard's tardiness is a sign that he stole the money?

    f. What is Janet's opinion of Richard?

    g. Why was Richard late?

    h. How would you describe Shannon?

    i. How do you think Shannon felt after Richard came in and gave her the change?

    j. What is a good title for this story?

8. The wind and rain whipped against the trees, sending branches crashing down everywhere. Stella peeked out the small window in the front door just in time to see a window shutter land on the roof of the car. Just then the lights flickered on and off. Then everything was dark. Fortunately, the family was prepared. They had been tracking the storm for days and had plenty of time to stock up on batteries, candles, and ice.

By the next morning, everything was calm. Stella ventured outside with her dad to survey the scene. Stella gasped. A huge tree lay on top of their garage. The back window of their car was smashed. A live wire danced in the street. They could hear sirens wailing in the distance. Stella's dad hugged her tightly. "I sure am lucky," he said. "Everything I value is unharmed."

    a. What type of storm is it, and how do you know this?

    b. When the story opens, what time of day is it?

    c. What does "tracking the storm" mean?

    d. Why did the family stock up on batteries, candles, and ice?

    e. How could a wire dance in the street?

    f. What would be an unwise thing for Stella and her dad to do outside?

    g. Why did Stella and her dad hear sirens?

    h. What did Stella's dad mean when he said, "Everything I value is unharmed"?

    i. What do you think Stella and her dad did next?

    j. What is a good title for this story?

I.E.P. Objective: The client will answer interpretive questions from short stories with 90% or greater accuracy.

Task E: Drawing Inferences from Stories

Listen to (or read) each story. Then answer the questions.

1. "I'm sorry!" cried Alex. "I only took my eyes off him for a minute. But someone left the gate open, and he ran out before I could stop him."

   "It's okay," said his dad. "It could have happened to anyone. Luckily the car that hit him wasn't going very fast. The vet just called and said we can bring Max home now. His broken leg will heal, but he won't be chasing cars for a long time."

   a. What kind of animal is Max, and how do you know Max is an animal?

   b. How do you know that Alex is upset?

   c. How can you tell that Alex's dad didn't blame him for the accident?

   d. What do you think happened right before this paragraph?

   e. What do you think happens next?

   f. What would you change or add to this story?

2. "Table two needs another soda, and four is ready to order."

   "I'm on it," replied Julie. As she turned quickly, grabbing her tray, Julie tripped over Darius who was kneeling down to pick up a broken glass. As she fell, the tray flew out of Julie's hands and hit Sunny in the back. Startled, Sunny jostled the pitcher of water she held, and it splashed onto the head of a man sitting at a nearby table. His dinner partner began to laugh hysterically.

   a. Where do Julie and Sunny work, and what are their jobs?

   b. What does Julie mean when she says, "I'm on it"?

   c. What do you think Sunny will say to the man she splashed the water on?

   d. How do you think the man with the wet head will react?

   e. How could this chain of events have been prevented?

   f. What do you think happens next?

3. "I'm starving," moaned Mike. "I don't think I can make it another minute without some food!"

   "Well, you knew this was going to be a challenging adventure when you signed on," answered Ray.

I.E.P. Objective: The client will make inferences from short stories with 90% or greater accuracy.

Task E: Drawing Inferences from Stories, *continued*

"Sign on?" Mike replied. "I was drafted because you needed a foursome. The heat and the mosquitoes are terrible, not to mention the blister I'm getting on my hand. How much longer will it be until we reach the end?"

"I can't take it anymore!" yelled Rita. "I can see the windmill on the last hole from here. Quit your bellyaching and putt, will you?"

  a. What are Mike, Ray, and Rita doing?

  b. Do you think Mike chose this activity? Why?

  c. Are all the players mentioned by name? How do you know this?

  d. What is causing Mike to get a blister on his hand?

  e. What does "bellyaching" mean?

  f. What do you think happens next?

4. "It's raining cats and dogs out there. I'd better bring my umbrella," said Anna as she ran for the door. "If I hurry, I might make it to work on time." Anna slammed the front door and hurried down the walkway, dodging puddles as she walked to the bus stop. Suddenly a big gust of wind caught Anna's umbrella, turning her into a modern-day Mary Poppins. As she struggled to get control of her umbrella, Anna looked up to see her bus pull away from the stop and head on toward town.

  a. What does Anna mean by the phrase "raining cats and dogs"?

  b. Who is Anna talking to?

  c. Is Anna a child or an adult? How do you know?

  d. What does "dodging puddles" mean, and why was Anna doing this?

  e. How is Anna like Mary Poppins?

  f. What do you think Anna did after she saw her bus leave?

5. Dana's mom was helping Dana make her bed when they felt the house shake for a few moments. "Wow, that was a big truck!" said Dana.

Her mom glanced out the front window. "No," she said. "There are no trucks in sight. Run and look out the back window."

Dana ran to her brother's room and looked out, but the road behind the house was empty. She felt something sharp under her foot and bent down to pick up the pieces of her brother's soccer trophy. Just then the phone rang. It was Dana's cousin who lived about two miles away. Her cousin said, "You won't believe what just happened!"

I.E.P. Objective: The client will make inferences from short stories with 90% or greater accuracy.

     a. Why did Dana look for a truck after the house shook?

     b. On which side of the house are Dana's room and her brother's room located?

     c. What do you think caused the house to shake?

     d. Why was her brother's soccer trophy in pieces?

     e. Why is the distance between Dana's house and her cousin's house a clue as to what happened?

     f. What do you think Dana's cousin says next?

6. The bell rang and the children spilled out into the hallway. "How did you do?" asked Maria.

   Joan looked down at the floor and said, "I don't want to talk about it."

   "Well, I thought it was a piece of cake," replied Maria. "I'm glad I didn't spend too much time studying."

   Just then Mr. Conway came to the door, frowning and holding a paper. "Maria," he said. "I need to see you for a minute." Maria's smile faded as she walked back inside the classroom.

     a. Where are Maria and Joan, and how do you know this?

     b. What are Maria and Joan discussing?

     c. Why do you think Joan looked down at the floor?

     d. What does Maria mean when she says, "It was a piece of cake"?

     e. Why do you think Mr. Conway was frowning?

     f. What would you change or add to this story?

7. As the days grew shorter and the wind grew colder, Mother checked the food she had gathered during the harvest. "I hope there is enough," she thought. "Once this is gone, we won't be able to get any more until spring." She watched her children scurry through the leaves, laughing and tumbling as they chased each other up and down trees and under the haystack. "Have fun today," she called. "I smell snow in the air. Tomorrow we must go into the burrow." Hearing this, the children's faces fell, for they knew the long, dark time would soon be upon them.

     a. Why can't Mother get any more food until spring?

     b. What type of family could this be? How do you know it is not a human family?

I.E.P. Objective: The client will make inferences from short stories with 90% or greater accuracy.

    c. Could human children have played the same games?

    d. What is meant by "the children's faces fell"?

    e. What is the long, dark time?

    f. If the children answered Mother, what might they say?

8. Early Wednesday morning, John looked out the window and saw Mrs. Carter running down the street in her bathrobe, carrying a brown paper bag. "Hilda, the morning Olympics have begun!" hollered John with a laugh.

"What did Adam forget this time?" asked Hilda.

"Well, it's a small, brown bag. Must be his lunch," replied John.

"It might do that child good to go without lunch for a change. Maybe it would improve his memory," observed Hilda.

"Look who's talking," said John. "I remember when Timmy forgot his science poster, and you were late for work because you dropped it off at school on your way."

    a. What is the relationship between John and Hilda?

    b. What does John mean by "the morning Olympics"?

    c. How does Hilda know that Adam has forgotten something?

    d. Who is Timmy?

    e. How do you think Hilda replied to John's last statement to her?

    f. What information is missing about Adam, Mrs. Carter, and the lunch bag?

9. Carl's heart rate was right on target, and he was starting to work up a sweat. He had been walking about ten minutes when suddenly he began to speed up. Next he stumbled and jumped to the floor. Looking a little embarrassed, he stood up and rubbed his elbow. Mr. Santos hurried over and asked what had happened. "It just started speeding up on its own. I tried to slow it down, but the button is stuck. I had to jump off while it was still moving."

"I'm sorry," Mr. Santos replied. "I'll write up a repair order. I hope you're okay."

"Well, I bumped my elbow, but I don't think anything is broken," observed Carl.

I.E.P. Objective: The client will make inferences from short stories with 90% or greater accuracy.

a. Where is Carl, and how do you know this?

b. What was Carl doing before he jumped to the floor?

c. What happened to Carl when he jumped to the floor?

d. Why did Carl rub his elbow, and why was he embarrassed?

e. Who is Mr. Santos, and why is he going to write up a repair order?

f. What is another way this story could have ended?

10. Anthony raced across the front yard and up the steps. A dog inside the house barked excitedly. Anthony grabbed a bag from the front porch, ran back to the van, and jumped inside. "Quick, shut the door!" said the driver as he drove to the next house. "Do you see anything on this porch?" he asked.

"No, but there's something on the one across the street," observed Tyrone. "I'll grab it!"

"The van's full, but we can probably fit in one more bag," said Anthony.

"Great! Let's get rid of this load and go to the next block," said the driver. "Our troop might collect the most food today. We can restock the bank with all of these donations!"

a. Why are the boys taking bags from porches?

b. Why are they in a hurry?

c. What kind of troop might the boys belong to?

d. What kind of bank are they going to restock?

e. At the beginning of the paragraph, what did you think the boys were doing?

f. What do you think happens next?

I.E.P. Objective: The client will make inferences from short stories with 90% or greater accuracy.

Task F: Describing and Interpreting Pictures

Look at the picture and respond to the following:

1. Explain what is happening in this picture.
2. What happened immediately before this picture?
3. What do you think will happen next?
4. Ask a *why* question about this picture.
5. Ask an *if/what would happen if* question about this picture.
6. Ask a *how* question about this picture.
7. Ask a *should/could/would* question about this picture.
8. Suggest a title for this scene.

I.E.P. Objective: The client will describe and interpret events in picture scenes with 90% or greater accuracy.

96

Task F: Describing and Interpreting Pictures, *continued*

Look at the picture and respond to the following:

1. Explain what is happening in this picture.
2. What happened immediately before this picture?
3. What do you think will happen next?
4. Ask a *why* question about this picture.
5. Ask an *if/what would happen if* question about this picture.
6. Ask a *how* question about this picture.
7. Ask a *should/could/would* question about this picture.
8. Suggest a title for this scene.

I.E.P. Objective: The client will describe and interpret events in picture scenes with 90% or greater accuracy.

Task F: Describing and Interpreting Pictures, *continued*

Look at the picture and respond to the following:

1. Explain what is happening in this picture.
2. What happened immediately before this picture?
3. What do you think will happen next?
4. Ask a *why* question about this picture.
5. Ask an *if/what would happen if* question about this picture.
6. Ask a *how* question about this picture.
7. Ask a *should/could/would* question about this picture.
8. Suggest a title for this scene.

I.E.P. Objective: The client will describe and interpret events in picture scenes with 90% or greater accuracy.

Task F: Describing and Interpreting Pictures, *continued*

Look at the picture and respond to the following:

1. Explain what is happening in this picture.
2. What happened immediately before this picture?
3. What do you think will happen next?
4. Ask a *why* question about this picture.
5. Ask an *if/what would happen if* question about this picture.
6. Ask a *how* question about this picture.
7. Ask a *should/could/would* question about this picture.
8. Suggest a title for this scene.

I.E.P. Objective: The client will describe and interpret events in picture scenes with 90% or greater accuracy.

Task F: Describing and Interpreting Pictures, *continued*

Look at the picture and respond to the following:

1. Explain what is happening in this picture.
2. What happened immediately before this picture?
3. What do you think will happen next?
4. Ask a *why* question about this picture.
5. Ask an *if/what would happen if* question about this picture.
6. Ask a *how* question about this picture.
7. Ask a *should/could/would* question about this picture.
8. Suggest a title for this scene.

I.E.P. Objective: The client will describe and interpret events in picture scenes with 90% or greater accuracy.

Task F: Describing and Interpreting Pictures, *continued*

Look at the picture and respond to the following:

1. Explain what is happening in this picture.
2. What happened immediately before this picture?
3. What do you think will happen next?
4. Ask a *why* question about this picture.
5. Ask an *if/what would happen if* question about this picture.
6. Ask a *how* question about this picture.
7. Ask a *should/could/would* question about this picture.
8. Suggest a title for this scene.

I.E.P. Objective: The client will describe and interpret events in picture scenes with 90% or greater accuracy.

Task A: Formulating Situation-Specific Statements

Make up a statement or two for each situation. Respond as if you are speaking to someone.

What would you say to . . .

1. ask a friend to return some money he borrowed two weeks ago

   _____

2. ask where to find the ketchup in the grocery store

   _____

3. caution a young child to stay in the yard while playing ball

   _____

4. invite a friend to your home for dinner tomorrow evening

   _____

5. inform the clerk that he did not give you the correct change

   _____

6. remind your friend that you have plans to go out together tomorrow

   _____

7. caution your brother/children not to enter your room while you are away

   _____

8. tell the teacher she did not assign the homework she is trying to collect

   _____

9. encourage your friend to try out for the soccer team/apply for a new job

   _____

10. inquire about a jacket you left at a football game

    _____

11. prevent someone from sitting on a broken park bench

    _____

12. explain to a salesclerk that you want to exchange some shoes for a larger size

    _____

13. inform your teacher/boss that you are moving in one week

    _____

I.E.P. Objective: The client will formulate appropriate statements for specific situations with 90% accuracy.

Task A: Formulating Situation-Specific Statements, *continued*

Make up a statement or two for each situation. Respond as if you are speaking to someone.

14. inquire why there is no one swimming in the ocean today

_____

15. tell a child at the movies that she is sitting in your seat

_____

16. describe your car to a parking lot attendant

_____

17. convince someone to buy a dictionary from your yard sale

_____

18. sign up volunteers for a neighborhood cleanup

_____

19. ask someone to move his car from behind your car

_____

20. express your thanks for a gift that you really like

_____

21. express your thanks for a gift that you do not like

_____

22. discourage your neighbor from playing loud music late at night

_____

23. inquire why your newspaper hasn't been delivered for the past three days

_____

24. explain to a friend that you have changed your mind about going out this evening

_____

25. warn a companion that she is about to step in a hole

_____

26. tell the receptionist in an office that she is pronouncing your name incorrectly

_____

I.E.P. Objective: The client will formulate appropriate statements for specific situations with 90% accuracy.

Make up a statement or two for each situation. Respond as if you are speaking to someone.

27. explain to the nurse how you cut your foot

_____

28. instruct a child how to cross the street safely

_____

29. ask a passenger in your car if it is safe to back out of a parking space

_____

30. persuade the librarian not to charge you for an overdue book

_____

31. direct someone from your house or apartment to the nearest grocery store

_____

32. inform someone that his dog must be on a leash while in the park

_____

33. describe your house/apartment to someone who has never seen it

_____

34. persuade a friend not to repeat a secret you have told her

_____

35. discourage an acquaintance from calling your home late at night

_____

36. convince a family member to let you drive his brand new car

_____

37. express your concern about a friend's bad habit

_____

38. console a friend over the loss of a pet

_____

39. persuade an acquaintance to vote for the candidate you support

_____

I.E.P. Objective: The client will formulate appropriate statements for specific situations with 90% accuracy.

Applying Language Skills
Task B: Interpreting Subtle Meanings

Give the underlying (implied) meaning of each statement or question in your own words.
The first one is done for you.

1. Do you think it's cold in here?
   I'm cold.

2. Isn't it about time for your dad to pick you up?

3. All this talk is making me thirsty!

4. These grocery bags are very heavy!

5. Are you going to finish that bag of popcorn?

6. How can you see well enough to read in here?

7. I know I left a candy bar in the cupboard. Do you know what happened to it?

8. Kevin, it hurts my back when you kick the back of my chair.

9. Let's give someone else a turn to talk.

10. Jerry, how about saving some cookies for the rest of us?

11. I won't be able to vacuum your room with all those papers on the floor.

12. That looks just like the pen I left in this desk yesterday.

13. Those strawberries look so juicy!

I.E.P. Objective: The client will paraphrase statements to convey underlying meaning with 90% or greater accuracy.

Give the underlying (implied) meaning of each statement or question in your own words.

14.   I'm trusting you with the only key we have to the back door.

_____

15.   I would hate for that new toy to get stepped on and broken.

_____

16.   Your horse sure looks thirsty.

_____

17.   It's difficult to hear the speaker when everyone is talking.

_____

18.   When's the last time you washed this car?

_____

19.   I'm not sure I can be ready by two o'clock.

_____

20.   You must have stayed up late last night!

_____

21.   I guess you didn't get the message to call me before 9:00.

_____

22.   Are you sure you got a point on your turn?

_____

23.   Did you forget to add sugar to this lemonade?

_____

24.   Sandra likes to be in charge of everyone.

_____

25.   We can invite Ella if you insist.

_____

26.   How did I like the play? Well, it was different.

_____

I.E.P. Objective: The client will paraphrase statements to convey underlying meaning with 90% or greater
          accuracy.

HELP for Language   106

Task B: Interpreting Subtle Meanings, *continued*

Give the underlying (implied) meaning of each statement or question in your own words.

27. I've been in charge of the meetings for a year. I should give someone else a turn.

_____

28. I'd like to buy this car from you but the price is too high.

_____

29. Dad, did you know that all my friends are going to the movies on Saturday? It sounds like so much fun!

_____

30. That's my coat on the back of your chair. I left it there when I got up for a minute.

_____

31. Your dog must have had insomnia last night!

_____

32. Did you get stuck in traffic on the way to work?

_____

33. I heard you had a party for Doug. I would have loved to have been there.

_____

34. Your cousin is cute. Does he have a girlfriend?

_____

35. How do you like your new hot tub? We're thinking of getting one, but we're not sure what kind is best.

_____

36. You are really skilled at finding every little error in my work.

_____

37. I just washed the kitchen floor, but the front door is unlocked.

_____

38. Do you want any change back?

_____

39. You certainly got up bright and early this morning to call me!

_____

I.E.P. Objective: The client will paraphrase statements to convey underlying meaning with 90% or greater accuracy.

Task C: Discriminating Between Literal and Rhetorical Questions

Listen to (or read) each question and decide if it needs an answer. The first one is done for you.

1. Where did you put the lid to the jelly? (answer) no answer

2. Can you believe it's raining again? answer no answer

3. Why is the broom in the sink? answer no answer

4. How much time do we have? answer no answer

5. Now what did I do with my backpack? answer no answer

6. Are you out to lunch? answer no answer

7. Where are the bagels? answer no answer

8. Do you think I'm made of money? answer no answer

9. When did Jackie leave? answer no answer

10. Why don't you just leave me alone? answer no answer

11. Did anyone feed the cat today? answer no answer

12. What in the world could be in this box? answer no answer

13. How many times have I told you to move your bike? answer no answer

14. Do you want to come to the movies with me? answer no answer

15. Have you ever heard anything so ridiculous? answer no answer

16. Do you think this rope is long enough? answer no answer

17. What is this world coming to? answer no answer

18. Do you think I have eyes in the back of my head? answer no answer

19. Should I invite Carlos too? answer no answer

20. Aren't you the lucky one? answer no answer

21. Could this movie be any duller? answer no answer

I.E.P. Objective: The client will discriminate between literal and rhetorical questions with 90% accuracy.

Task C: Discriminating Between Literal and Rhetorical Questions, *continued*

Listen to (or read) each question and decide if it needs an answer.

22.	Aren't you Sally Richmond's daughter?	answer	no answer
23.	What date are you planning to move?	answer	no answer
24.	What was I thinking?	answer	no answer
25.	Aren't you adorable?	answer	no answer
26.	Did the power go off while I was out?	answer	no answer
27.	Who wouldn't like to win $1,000?	answer	no answer
28.	Shouldn't we give Susie the list?	answer	no answer
29.	What was that all about?	answer	no answer
30.	Did you see the toad in the mailbox?	answer	no answer
31.	Do you think I was born yesterday?	answer	no answer
32.	Is he for real?	answer	no answer
33.	Who died and made you king (queen)?	answer	no answer
34.	Why didn't I get credit for this answer?	answer	no answer
35.	Do you think we'll get there before the party starts?	answer	no answer
36.	Could you have been any later?	answer	no answer
37.	Should I move my car from behind yours?	answer	no answer
38.	Can 36 be divided evenly by 12?	answer	no answer
39.	Can you make a little more noise while I nap?	answer	no answer
40.	Do you want to taste this new recipe?	answer	no answer
41.	How about those Patriots?	answer	no answer
42.	Where have you been all my life?	answer	no answer

I.E.P. Objective: The client will discriminate between literal and rhetorical questions with 90% accuracy.

Task D: Answering Personal Opinion Questions

Answer each question *yes* or *no* and tell why. There are no right or wrong answers.

1. Should children have to pay full price at the movies after 6:00 PM?

   _____

2. If you found a dollar on the sidewalk, would you keep it?

   _____

3. What time should a ten-year-old child go to bed on a school night?

   _____

4. Should TV stations show commercials only before or after shows?

   _____

5. Should children over the age of 12 be allowed to stay home alone?

   _____

6. Should sick students be allowed to come to school so they can have perfect attendance?

   _____

7. If a friend asks to take your valuable coin collection to school for a project, should you let him?

   _____

8. If a child breaks something inexpensive at your home, would you tell her parent?

   _____

9. If your telephone rings, must you answer it?

   _____

10. If you rent a movie but don't watch it, should you have to pay for it?

    _____

11. If a student is caught cheating on a test, should she get an **F**?

    _____

12. If an elderly person gets on a crowded subway, should you give him your seat?

    _____

13. If someone who doesn't know you mispronounces your name, should you tell her?

    _____

I.E.P. Objective: The client will provide personal opinions in response to questions on 90% of trials.

110

Task D: Answering Personal Opinion Questions, *continued*

Answer each question *yes* or *no* and tell why. There are no right or wrong answers.

14. If someone starts to tell you a joke you've already heard, should you stop him or let him go ahead and finish?

_____

15. Should surfers be allowed on the same beach as swimmers?

_____

16. Should preschool children be allowed to watch PG movies?

_____

17. If one team member for a group project does little of the work, should he get the same grade as the other team members?

_____

18. Should dogs be allowed to roam in their own neighborhoods without leashes?

_____

19. How old must a child be to choose his own clothes and hairstyle?

_____

20. Should there be laws that require drivers to pull off the road to use cell phones?

_____

21. Should a student be assigned to a different class if he doesn't like his teacher?

_____

22. Should people be allowed to bring food from home into movie theaters?

_____

23. If you receive junk mail in your mailbox addressed to someone else, is it okay to throw it away?

_____

24. Should 12-year-old children be allowed to spend the afternoon at the mall without an adult?

_____

25. If you're a dinner guest at someone's house and you find a bug in your soup, should you tell the host?

_____

I.E.P. Objective: The client will provide personal opinions in response to questions on 90% of trials.

111

Task D: Answering Personal Opinion Questions, *continued*

Answer each question *yes* or *no* and tell why. There are no right or wrong answers.

26. If a store runs out of an item that is advertised on sale, should you be able to buy the item at the sale price on another day?

    _____

27. Is it acceptable to bring more than 12 items to the "12 items or less" checkout line at the grocery store?

    _____

28. Should cars be charged less than SUVs on toll roads?

    _____

29. How long should you wait for someone before going into the movies without her?

    _____

30. If a good friend asks to borrow $50.00 but can't tell you why, should you lend him the money?

    _____

31. If you borrow a friend's car and it gets hit in a parking lot while you are in a store, who should pay for the damage not covered by insurance?

    _____

32. If you return an item to a store and it is now on sale for a lower price, should you get the full price refunded?

    _____

33. If you eat dinner at a restaurant and become sick the next day, should the restaurant refund your money?

    _____

34. If you are paying with cash at a store, should the clerk ask for your telephone number before he rings up your sale?

    _____

35. Should there be a law against sending junk mail or should anyone be allowed to mail information to anyone else if they pay the postage?

    _____

36. If the speed limit is 55 miles per hour, is it okay to drive 60 miles per hour?

    _____

I.E.P. Objective: The client will provide personal opinions in response to questions on 90% of trials.

Task E: Understanding Multiple-Meaning Words

Make up a sentence for the different meanings of each word below. The first one is done for you.

1. **fall**
   a season of the year: _Each fall we go apple picking._

   to trip and land on the ground: _____

   water cascading over a cliff: _____

2. **head**
   a body part: _____

   the person in charge: _____

   to go toward: _____

3. **miss**
   to fail to catch: _____

   longing for a person or place: _____

   an unmarried young woman: _____

4. **ring**
   jewelry worn on the finger: _____

   to sound a bell: _____

   a circle around an object: _____

5. **fly**
   a small insect: _____

   to soar through the air: _____

   the front opening of pants: _____

6. **trunk**
   an elephant's nose: _____

   a storage compartment in the back of a car: _____

   a large suitcase: _____

7. **toast**
   sliced bread browned by heat: _____

   to raise a glass in honor of someone: _____

   to warm food over a fire: _____

I.E.P. Objective: The client will use multiple-meaning words in sentences connoting their different meanings on 90% of trials.

Task E: Understanding Multiple-Meaning Words, *continued*

Make up a sentence for the different meanings of each word below.

8. **band**
   a group of musicians: _____

   a decorative stripe around an object: _____

   to join together: _____

9. **strike**
   to hit: _____

   to swing a bat and miss the ball: _____

   to stop working: _____

10. **match**
    a small piece of wood with a combustible tip: _____

    a sports competition: _____

    to be equal or similar: _____

11. **bill**
    a duck's beak: _____

    a statement of money owed: _____

    a proposed law: _____

12. **track**
    an oval running surface: _____

    footprints left by an animal: _____

    to follow something using clues or signals: _____

13. **block**
    a child's toy: _____

    to prevent from happening: _____

    a rectangular space enclosed by streets: _____

14. **seal**
    an official stamp: _____

    to close tightly: _____

    a sea mammal: _____

I.E.P. Objective: The client will use multiple-meaning words in sentences connoting their different meanings on 90% of trials.

Task E: Understanding Multiple-Meaning Words, *continued*

Make up a sentence for the different meanings of each word below.

15. **ground**
    smashed into small particles: _____

    the lowest floor of a building: _____

    dirt/earth: _____

16. **pick**
    to choose: _____

    to pluck the strings of a guitar: _____

    to steal from someone's pocket: _____

17. **note**
    a short letter: _____

    a tone of definite pitch in music: _____

    to notice or heed: _____

18. **right**
    opposed to left: _____

    lawful or proper: _____

    correct or suitable: _____

19. **spread**
    to lay out or stretch out: _____

    to distribute a thin layer of something on bread: _____

    a cloth covering for a table or bed: _____

20. **tie**
    to fasten by entwining a rope, string, or ribbon: _____

    to equal the score of an opponent: _____

    a narrow strip of cloth worn around the neck: _____

21. **cut**
    to make an opening with a knife or scissors: _____

    to divide a pack of cards after shuffling: _____

    an open wound: _____

I.E.P. Objective: The client will use multiple-meaning words in sentences connoting their different meanings on 90% of trials.

Task F: Interpreting Common Sayings (Idioms)

Choose the correct meaning of each statement. The first one is done for you.

1. Stop beating around the bush.

   a. Stop walking in circles.
   (b.) Say what you mean.
   c. Don't hit the roses!

2. Harold aced his Spanish test.

   a. Harold didn't finish the test.
   b. Harold got an A on the test.
   c. Harold failed his Spanish test.

3. You'd better face the music.

   a. Look at the piano now.
   b. This is a good deal.
   c. It's time to accept the punishment for what you did.

4. Ross flew off the handle.

   a. Ross really got mad.
   b. Ross was badly injured.
   c. Ross laughed hysterically.

5. I'm going to play it by ear.

   a. I'm going to follow the rules.
   b. I'll listen carefully to the instructions.
   c. I'll figure out what to do as I go.

6. We'd better toe the line at camp.

   a. We need to pull hard on the rope.
   b. We'd better draw a line on the ground.
   c. We'd better do what we are supposed to do.

7. I beat you to the punch!

   a. I got here first.
   b. I drank all the punch.
   c. I'm so mad at you.

8. Look before you leap!

   a. Be cautious when starting something new or unknown.
   b. Always have someone watch out for you when diving.
   c. Be careful in leap years because they are unlucky.

I.E.P. Objective: The client will identify the meanings of idioms with 90% accuracy.

Task F: Interpreting Common Sayings (Idioms), *continued*

Choose the correct meaning of each statement.

9.   I lost my shirt on that deal.

   a. My clothing got ripped off.
   b. It was a great deal.
   c. I lost a lot of money.

10.   The cat's out of the bag now.

   a. Hurry and catch the cat.
   b. It's no longer a secret.
   c. There's no cat food in the bag.

11.   Don't put all your eggs in one basket.

   a. Divide the eggs into two groups.
   b. Don't put all your efforts into one project.
   c. Be careful with fragile objects.

12.   He's got a dozen irons in the fire.

   a. He's in big trouble now.
   b. He's moved around a lot.
   c. He's got a lot of projects underway.

13.   I can't help you. My back is to the wall.

   a. I am leaning against the wall.
   b. Move forward so I have more room.
   c. There's nothing else I can do.

14.   It's six of one, half a dozen of the other.

   a. We have a dozen in all.
   b. The choices are about the same.
   c. You take half and I'll take half.

15.   I had the rug pulled out from under me.

   a. I was totally surprised.
   b. I tripped and fell down.
   c. I found what I was searching for.

16.   We finished the parade float at the eleventh hour.

   a. We finished the float at 11:00.
   b. We finished the float at the last minute.
   c. We finished the float too late for the parade.

I.E.P. Objective: The client will identify the meanings of idioms with 90% accuracy.

Task F: Interpreting Common Sayings (Idioms), *continued*

Choose the correct meaning of each statement.

17. I ride the train once in a blue moon.

    a. I ride the train infrequently.
    b. I ride the train only at night.
    c. I ride the train daily.

18. I'll be at your wedding come rain or shine.

    a. I won't come to your wedding if it rains.
    b. I'll come to your wedding if it doesn't rain.
    c. I'll come to your wedding no matter what happens.

19. When the last bell rang, it was music to my ears.

    a. I was glad the bell rang.
    b. I didn't hear the bell because of the music.
    c. I listened to music until the bell rang.

20. Our hosts rolled out the red carpet for us.

    a. Our hosts cleaned their carpet before we came.
    b. Our hosts did special things for us.
    c. Our hosts were unfriendly to us.

21. Don't bite off more than you can chew.

    a. Don't take on more than you can handle.
    b. Don't chew with your mouth open.
    c. Don't spread rumors about others.

22. Chris got a dirty look from his mom.

    a. Chris's mom had mud on her face.
    b. Chris's mom frowned at him.
    c. Chris's mom likes to work in her garden.

23. Don't bite the hand that feeds you.

    a. Be nice to those who help you.
    b. Be careful when feeding livestock.
    c. Help others by giving them food.

24. People who live in glass houses shouldn't throw stones.

    a. It is dangerous to throw stones at someone.
    b. People shouldn't lie to each other.
    c. You shouldn't criticize someone unless you are without fault.

I.E.P. Objective: The client will identify the meanings of idioms with 90% accuracy.

118

Task G: Choosing Fixed-Order Idioms

Choose the idiom that best completes each sentence. Then tell the meaning of the sentence.
The first one is done for you.

1. I am _____ of taking out the trash every day.

    tired and true   (sick and tired)   sick and old

    _____I am tired of taking out the trash._____

2. That's like comparing _____.

    apples and oranges   oranges and grapefruit   fruit and vegetables

    _____

3. I'll bring you a snack when I'm _____.

    good and better   good and ready   ready and waiting

    _____

4. I'll believe it when I see it in _____.

    black and blue   red, white, and blue   black and white

    _____

5. It's Carol, the _____ spelling bee champ!

    one and only   one and two   holy and only

    _____

6. You can't ignore the _____ truth.

    stupid and simple   plain and chocolate   plain and simple

    _____

7. The Hornets are _____ and ready to win!

    alive and dead   alive and kicking   kicking and screaming

    _____

*I.E.P. Objective: The client will choose fixed-order idioms to complete sentences and interpret their meanings
with 90% or greater accuracy.*

119

Task G: Choosing Fixed-Order Idioms, *continued*

Choose the idiom that best completes each sentence. Then tell the meaning of the sentence.

8.   It was _____ for a while, but Stanley is better now.

   touch and go   touch and tackle   go and find

   _____

9.   Let's have a _____ review of the chapter.

   filthy and dirty   quick and thick   quick and dirty

   _____

10.   Everyone must be willing to _____ if we want to get along.

   fight and kick   take and hide   give and take

   _____

11.   In summertime, the living is _____.

   hard and easy   rough and bumpy   free and easy

   _____

12.   I'm counting on you to mind your _____ while Grandma is visiting.

   dogs and cats   p's and q's   x, y, and z's

   _____

13.   If you borrow the car today, I'll be left _____.

   dark and dry   high and hot   high and dry

   _____

14.   If I don't find a job soon, I'll be _____.

   over and out   down and out   out and about

   _____

I.E.P. Objective: The client will choose fixed-order idioms to complete sentences and interpret their meanings with 90% or greater accuracy.

Task G: Choosing Fixed-Order Idioms, *continued*

Choose the idiom that best completes each sentence. Then tell the meaning of the sentence.

15. The graduation speech was _____.

        short and sweet   short and squatty   sweet and sour

_____

16. I know it's hot in here, but try to _____.

        grin and win   share it and bear it   grin and bear it

_____

17. When the horses rounded the last turn, they were _____.

        neck and neck   tail and tail   nose and nose

_____

18. I may be old-fashioned, but my way is _____.

        true and false   tried and trained   tried and true

_____

19. My lawyer says it's an _____ case.

        open-and-shut   open-and-ready   out-and-in

_____

20. A true friend will stick by you through _____.

        fat and thin   thick and juicy   thick and thin

_____

21. At the flea market, everything is _____.

        cash and trash   check and checkmate   cash and carry

_____

I.E.P. Objective: The client will choose fixed-order idioms to complete sentences and interpret their meanings
with 90% or greater accuracy.

HELP for Language   121

Task H: Completing and Interpreting Proverbs

Choose the best word to complete each proverb. Then tell what the proverb means in your own words. The first one is done for you.

1. Good fences make _____ neighbors.

       bad   (good)   next door

If you give your neighbors privacy, you will get along better.

2. There's no place like _____.

       Ireland   home   the kitchen

3. The _____ the limit.

       weight's   net's   sky's

4. They disappeared in the _____ of an eye.

       center   blink   blue

5. The early bird catches the _____.

       sun   worm   mouse

6. Waste not, _____ not.

       have   want   take

7. You can't _____ them all.

       win   find   hide

I.E.P. Objective: The client will complete and paraphrase proverbs with 90% accuracy.

Task H: Completing and Interpreting Proverbs, *continued*

Choose the best word to complete each proverb. Then tell what the proverb means in your own words.

8. Haste makes _____.

             mistakes   waste   wishes

    _____

9. _____ can't be choosers.

             Captains   Beggars   Horses

    _____

10. Better late than _____.

             early   dirty   never

    _____

11. When the _____ is away, the mice will play.

             cheese   cat   game

    _____

12. No _____, no gain.

             eat   fun   pain

    _____

13. Don't bite off more than you can _____.

             pay for   chew   lift

    _____

14. It's all in a day's _____.

             work   time   weather

    _____

I.E.P. Objective: The client will complete and paraphrase proverbs with 90% accuracy.

Task H: Completing and Interpreting Proverbs, *continued*

Choose the best word to complete each proverb. Then tell what the proverb means in your own words.

15. You can't please _____.

        Grandma   Louise   everyone

_____

16. United we _____; divided we fall.

        fly   rest   stand

_____

17. Two captains will _____ a ship.

        sink   build   fly

_____

18. Never say _____.

        never   stop   your name

_____

19. Seize the _____.

        handle   trees   day

_____

20. It takes one to know _____.

        how   one   nothing

_____

21. Don't sweat the _____ stuff.

        small   hot   new

_____

I.E.P. Objective: The client will complete and paraphrase proverbs with 90% accuracy.

Task H: Completing and Interpreting Proverbs, *continued*

Choose the best word to complete each proverb. Then tell what the proverb means in your own words.

22. Two wrongs don't make a _____.

        cake   choice   right

_____

23. Don't look a gift horse in the _____.

        mouth   saddle   night

_____

24. Too many _____ spoil the broth.

        cooks   carrots   cups

_____

25. Don't judge a book by its _____.

        color   author   cover

_____

26. _____ is only skin deep.

        Lotion   Kindness   Beauty

_____

27. You are what you _____.

        eat   watch   wear

_____

28. Every _____ has a silver lining.

        purse   cloud   jacket

_____

I.E.P. Objective: The client will complete and paraphrase proverbs with 90% accuracy.

Task I: Choosing Similes

Choose the best word to complete each statement. The first one is done for you.

1. Julia is as good as _____.

   mustard   (gold)   lace

2. The steps are as slippery as _____.

   glass   wood   shoes

3. The inside of our tent was as cold as _____.

   August   soup   ice

4. These cookies are as dry as _____.

   jelly   cardboard   rain

5. Fran loves the pool. She swims like a _____.

   rock   fish   cat

6. I can move this box. It's as light as a _____.

   feather   rainbow   stone

7. Ted will know the answer. He's as sharp as a _____.

   ruler   tack   watch

8. Our new puppy's fur is as soft as _____.

   cotton   rubber   plastic

9. The edge of this leaf is as sharp as a _____.

   knife   spoon   shoe

10. Our vacation was like a bad _____.

    check   dream   cold

I.E.P. Objective: The client will choose words to complete similes with 90% or greater accuracy.

Task I: Choosing Similes, *continued*

Choose the best word to complete each statement.

11. Ashley jumped up as fast as a _____.

          cat up a tree   turtle on a log   snail on a sidewalk

12. This bread is stale. It's as tough as _____.

          dandelions   jam   nails

13. I just washed the kitchen floor. It's as clean as a _____.

          whistle   bucket   well

14. Grandpa Al is ninety-nine. He's as old as the _____.

          coffee   porch   hills

15. As quick as a _____, Dad fixed the television.

          wheel   wink   tank

16. Kathryn is a soprano in the chorus. She sings like a _____.

          rocket   owl   canary

17. The new car's engine purrs like a _____.

          thermometer   kitten   saltine

18. The vet said our dog is as fit as a _____.

          fiddle   drum   boot

19. Sal moved the refrigerator without help. He is as strong as an _____.

          artichoke   ox   urn

20. Kim placed first in every race. She's as fast as a _____.

          deer   mule   rhino

I.E.P. Objective: The client will choose words to complete similes with 90% or greater accuracy.

Task I: Choosing Similes, *continued*

Choose the best word to complete each statement.

21. After swimming 100 laps, Maria was as limp as a _____.

            cane   rag doll   wire hanger

22. When I jump on the trampoline, I soar like an _____.

            eagle   elephant   eel

23. When Steven goes to a restaurant, he eats like a _____.

            horse   snail   mouse

24. Trevor tried to help me but his directions were as clear as _____.

            rain   mud   icicles

25. After a long day at work, Sharon slept like a _____.

            banana   clock   baby

26. Marcus' skateboard is like a magic _____.

            trick   carpet   number

27. On Saturdays, we are as busy as a dog with _____.

            fleas   a leash   crackers

28. This game is as dangerous as a pool of _____.

            minnows   clams   sharks

29. The plans for the party are as secret as a _____.

            mailbox   trap door   stop sign

30. The broken fan is as still as a _____.

            frozen waterfall   spinning top   tidal wave

I.E.P. Objective: The client will choose words to complete similes with 90% or greater accuracy.

Applying Language Skills
Task J: Completing Similes

Think of a word or words to complete each statement. The first one is done for you.

1. Lulu is as sweet as _____*molasses*_____.

2. Buddy is as strong as an _____.

3. Grandma's biscuits are as light as a _____.

4. The cowboy's hands were as tough as _____.

5. Hannah runs as fast as the _____.

6. The water in the pool was as cold as _____.

7. When I run through the field I am as free as a _____.

8. The refrigerator sounds as loud as a _____.

9. Mr. Bartley is as old as the _____.

10. This job is as easy as _____.

11. Our new dog is as ferocious as a _____.

12. The instructions on the box were as clear as _____.

13. Chuck is as sick as a _____.

14. After tilling the garden, Gramps was as dirty as a _____.

15. The children in the library are as quiet as _____.

16. My love for you is as deep as the _____.

17. These old rolls are as hard as _____.

18. The cat's claws are as sharp as _____.

19. When Dad saw the dent in the fender he was as mad as a _____.

20. Since early this morning, I've been as busy as a _____.

21. After their parents left the children were as wild as _____.

I.E.P. Objective: The client will complete similes with 90% or greater accuracy.

Task J: Completing Similes, *continued*

Think of a word or words to complete each statement.

22. When I got out of the bathtub my fingers were as wrinkled as _____.

23. This old house is as solid as a _____.

24. Uncle Roger is as jolly as a _____.

25. After I sanded the board it felt as smooth as _____.

26. Thomas's face is as green as _____.

27. This medicine tastes as sour as _____.

28. The button on this cell phone is as small as an _____.

29. The sunflowers in the garden are as tall as the _____.

30. While hiding, I stood as still as a _____.

31. The colt's legs are as skinny as _____.

32. When I reached the attic, it was as hot as an _____.

33. My baby sister is as cute as a _____.

34. When I found my wallet I was as happy as a _____.

35. Princess Pat is as pretty as a _____.

36. My grandmother is as lucky as a _____.

37. Joshua's eyes are as blue as the _____.

38. This backpack is as heavy as a _____.

39. Devon woke up as grumpy as a _____.

40. When I took the cake from the oven it was as flat as a _____.

41. If I skip lunch, by 4:00 I'm as hungry as a _____.

42. This old horse is as gentle as a _____.

I.E.P. Objective: The client will complete similes with 90% or greater accuracy.

Applying Language Skills
Task K: Explaining Metaphors

Explain what each statement means. The first one is done for you.

1. Education is the key to success.
    _____ *A good education will help you do other things, such as get a job.* _____

2. Her room is a pigpen.
    _____

3. Jill is the class clown.
    _____

4. My feet are two frozen blocks of ice.
    _____

5. David is a walking encyclopedia.
    _____

6. The brain is a toolbox.
    _____

7. Grandma's garden is a rainbow.
    _____

8. Her smile is a ray of sunshine.
    _____

9. Children's minds are sponges.
    _____

10. The puppies are a barrel of laughs.
    _____

11. This car is a dinosaur.
    _____

12. Our classroom is a zoo.
    _____

13. Kelly's hair is a bird's nest in the mornings.
    _____

I.E.P. Objective: The client will paraphrase metaphors with 90% accuracy.

Task K: Explaining Metaphors, *continued*

Explain what each statement means.

14. The children were bees swarming the ice-cream truck.

_____

15. A good teacher is a ringmaster.

_____

16. Cara is a breath of fresh air in our office.

_____

17. The new baby is a gift.

_____

18. That old horse is a bag of bones.

_____

19. Laughter is the best medicine.

_____

20. The twins are two peas in a pod.

_____

21. Time is money.

_____

22. Our backyard is a jungle.

_____

23. The sound of the car in the driveway was music to my ears.

_____

24. Every day is a winding road.

_____

25. This overdue bill is a thorn in my side.

_____

26. Tyra is a magnet for bad luck.

_____

I.E.P. Objective: The client will paraphrase metaphors with 90% accuracy.

Task K: Explaining Metaphors, *continued*

Explain what each statement means.

27. Beagles are the clowns of the dog world.

    _____

28. His grandson's visit was the best medicine.

    _____

29. Spring is a jack-in-the-box waiting to pop.

    _____

30. The cow field is a land mine.

    _____

31. Wooly caterpillars are the weather forecasters of the forest.

    _____

32. The hurricane was a bulldozer rumbling through our neighborhood.

    _____

33. Mr. Rolfe is a font of knowledge.

    _____

34. Hard work is the cornerstone of success.

    _____

35. Dad is the bedrock of our family.

    _____

36. Pain is her constant companion.

    _____

37. All the world is a stage.

    _____

38. Space is the final frontier.

    _____

39. Our eyes are the windows to our souls.

    _____

I.E.P. Objective: The client will paraphrase metaphors with 90% accuracy.

HELP for Language   133

Task L: Choosing Meanings of Different Intonations

Stress the bold word as you read each statement aloud. Then choose the correct meaning of the statement. (*Note: You may choose to read the statement to your clients.*)

1. "**You** didn't tell me you had to work late today!"
    a. Someone else told me you had to work late.
    b. You forgot to tell me you had to work late.
    c. You told someone else you had to work late.

2. "You didn't tell **me** you had to work late today!"
    a. Someone else told me you had to work late.
    b. You forgot to tell me you had to work late.
    c. You told someone else you had to work late.

3. "You didn't tell me you had to work late **today**!"
    a. Someone else told me you had to work late.
    b. You told me you had to work late tomorrow.
    c. You forgot to tell me you had to work late.

4. Did you see **Susan's** outfit at the dance?
    a. Were you one of the people who saw Susan's outfit?
    b. Did you see Susan's outfit or someone else's outfit?
    c. Can you believe what Susan wore to the dance?

5. Did you **see** Susan's outfit at the dance?
    a. Can you believe what Susan wore to the dance?
    b. Were you one of the people who saw Susan's outfit?
    c. Did you see Susan's outfit or someone else's?

6. My watch says it's almost **five**-fifteen.
    a. I thought it was four-fifteen, not five-fifteen.
    b. It's not quite five-fifteen.
    c. It's five-fifteen according to my watch, not someone else's.

7. My watch says it's **almost** five-fifteen.
    a. My watch says it's almost five-fifteen, not six-fifteen.
    b. It's not quite five-fifteen.
    c. It's five-fifteen according to my watch, not someone else's.

8. **My** watch says it's almost five-fifteen.
    a. It's not quite five-fifteen.
    b. I thought it was four-fifteen, not five-fifteen.
    c. It's five-fifteen according to my watch, not someone else's.

I.E.P. Objective: The client will choose the implied meanings of identical sentences with different intonations with 90% or greater accuracy.

Task L: Choosing Meanings of Different Intonations, *continued*

Stress the bold word as you read each statement aloud. Then choose the correct meaning of the statement.

9. **Noah** is sitting next to Scott's brother.
    a. Noah, not John, is sitting there.
    b. Noah is sitting beside Scott's brother, not his sister.
    c. Noah is sitting next to Scott's brother, not Al's brother.

10. Noah is sitting next to Scott's **brother**.
    a. Noah, not John, is sitting there.
    b. Noah is sitting beside Scott's brother, not his sister.
    c. Noah is sitting next to Scott's brother, not Al's brother.

11. Noah is sitting next to **Scott's** brother.
    a. Noah, not John, is sitting there.
    b. Noah is sitting next to Scott's brother, not Al's brother.
    c. Noah is sitting beside Scott's brother, not his sister.

12. If you had **worn** your poncho, you would not have gotten wet.
    a. If you had worn your poncho instead of your sweatshirt, you would not have gotten wet.
    b. If you had worn your poncho instead of your little brother's poncho, you would not have gotten wet.
    c. If you had put your poncho on, you would not have gotten wet.

13. If you had worn **your** poncho, you would not have gotten wet.
    a. If you had put your poncho on, you would not have gotten wet.
    b. If you had worn your poncho instead of your sweatshirt, you would not have gotten wet.
    c. If you had worn your poncho instead of your little brother's poncho, you would not have gotten wet.

14. If you had worn your **poncho**, you would not have gotten wet.
    a. If you had put your poncho on, you would not have gotten wet.
    b. If you had worn your poncho instead of your sweatshirt, you would not have gotten wet.
    c. If you had worn your poncho instead of your little brother's poncho, you would not have gotten wet.

15. There are no **bagels** left in the paper bag.
    a. There are more doughnuts in the bag, but no bagels.
    b. There are some bagels in the plastic bag, but not in the paper bag.
    c. I'm sure. There are no bagels left in the bag.

I.E.P. Objective: The client will choose the implied meanings of identical sentences with different intonations with 90% or greater accuracy.

Task L: Choosing Meanings of Different Intonations, *continued*

Stress the bold word as you read each statement aloud. Then choose the correct meaning of the statement.

16. There **are** no bagels left in the paper bag.
    a. There are some doughnuts left, but no bagels.
    b. There are some bagels in the plastic bag, but not in the paper bag.
    c. I'm sure. There are no bagels left in the bag.

17. There are no bagels left in the **paper** bag.
    a. If you look under the paper bag, there are some bagels.
    b. There are some bagels in the plastic bag, but not in the paper bag.
    c. I'm sure. There are no bagels left in the bag.

18. I will never again try to drive to Cincinnati in **one** day!
    a. I might try to drive to another city, but not to Cincinnati.
    b. I will try again, but take more than one day.
    c. I will never try it again for any reason.

19. I will never again try to drive to **Cincinnati** in one day!
    a. I will try again, but take more than one day.
    b. I might try to fly, but I won't try to drive.
    c. I will try to drive to other cities, but not Cincinnati.

20. **I** will never again try to drive to Cincinnati in one day!
    a. Other people may try it, but I won't.
    b. I will try to drive to Cleveland, but not Cincinnati.
    c. If I drive to Cincinnati, I will take more than one day.

21. **Green** apples make the best pies.
    a. Green apples, not red or yellow, make the best pies.
    b. Green apples, not green tomatoes or pears, make the best pies.
    c. Green apples make the best pies, not cakes.

22. Green apples make the best **pies**.
    a. Green apples, not green tomatoes or pears, make the best pies.
    b. Green apples make the best pies, not cakes.
    c. Green apples make the best pies, not the worst pies.

23. Green **apples** make the best pies.
    a. Green apples, not red or yellow, make the best pies.
    b. Green apples make the best pies, not the worst pies.
    c. Green apples, not green tomatoes or pears, make the best pies.

I.E.P. Objective: The client will choose the implied meanings of identical sentences with different intonations with 90% or greater accuracy.

Task M: Stating Meanings of Different Intonations

Read each sentence aloud, stressing the bold word. Then tell what the sentence means.

1. You **didn't** tell me that!
   You didn't tell **me** that!
   You didn't tell me that!

2. **She** never sits with us on the bus.
   She never sits with **us** on the bus.
   She never sits with us on the **bus**.

3. Is **this** the way to the library?
   Is this the way to the **library**?
   Is this the way **to** the library?

4. You put **salt** in the tea?
   You put salt in the tea?
   You put salt in the **tea**?

5. Nora **almost** dropped my plate.
   Nora almost dropped my plate.
   Nora almost dropped my **plate**.

6. The book costs **about** twelve dollars.
   The book costs about **twelve** dollars.
   The **book** costs about twelve dollars.

7. **Why** did he come home?
   Why did **he** come home?
   Why did he come **home**?

8. There are **no** spoons in the drawer.
   There are no **spoons** in the drawer.
   There are no spoons in the **drawer**.

9. Fluffy is my **cat's** name!
   Fluffy is my cat's name.
   Fluffy is **my** cat's name.

10. I told you the meeting was on **Thursday**.
    I **told** you the meeting was on Thursday.
    I told you the **meeting** was on Thursday.

I.E.P. Objective: The client will stress different words when reading sentences aloud and state the meaning for each sentence with 90% or greater accuracy.

137

Task M: Stating Meanings of Different Intonations, *continued*

Read each sentence aloud, stressing the bold word. Then tell what the sentence means.

11. The **strawberries** are too ripe to eat.
    The strawberries **are** too ripe to eat.
    The strawberries are too **ripe** to eat.

12. Why is a **ribbon** tied to the mailbox?
    Why is a ribbon tied to the **mailbox**?
    Why is a ribbon tied to the mailbox?

13. Helen misses school **every** Monday.
    Helen misses school every **Monday**.
    Helen misses school every Monday.

14. If you drop it, you **will** have to pay for it.
    If **you** drop it, **you** will have to pay for it.
    If you **drop** it, you will have to pay for it.

15. The **Chipmunks** are the best team!
    The Chipmunks **are** the best team!
    The Chipmunks are **the** best team!

16. Did I tell you the **whole** story?
    Did I tell **you** the whole story?
    Did **I** tell you the whole story?

17. **Karen** left early.
    Karen left **early**.
    Karen **left** early.

18. Did **Austin** get on the school bus?
    Did Austin get **on** the school bus?
    Did Austin get on the **school** bus?

19. **Lizzie** never feeds our dog.
    Lizzie never **feeds** our dog.
    Lizzie never feeds our **dog**.

20. The **highest** grade on the history exam was 72!
    The highest grade on the **history** exam was 72!
    The highest grade on the history exam was 72!

I.E.P. Objective: The client will stress different words when reading sentences aloud and state the meaning for each sentence with 90% or greater accuracy.

Applying Language Skills
Task N: Explaining Choices

Make a choice for each situation and explain why.

1. If I had to choose between driving a car or a motorcycle, I would choose _____

   because _____.

2. If I had to choose between playing jump rope or kickball at recess, I would choose _____

   because _____.

3. If I had to choose between sleeping in a tent or a treehouse, I would choose _____

   because _____.

4. If I had to choose between giving or receiving a gift, I would choose _____

   because _____.

5. If I had to choose between sweeping the sidewalk and vacuuming the bedrooms, I would

   choose _____ because _____.

6. If I had to choose between forgetting my sunglasses or my watch when going to the park,

   I would choose _____ because _____

   _____.

7. If I had to choose between becoming a farmer or a fisherman, I would choose _____

   because _____.

8. If I had to choose between being a tightrope walker or a lion tamer, I would choose

   _____ because _____.

9. If I had to choose between being the catcher or pitcher in a softball game, I would choose

   _____ because _____.

10. If I had to choose between sitting in the first row or the last row of a movie theater, I would

    choose _____ because _____.

11. If I had to choose between walking in the rain or the snow, I would choose _____

    because _____.

I.E.P. Objective: The client will choose between hypothetical situations and state a reason for each choice with 90% accuracy.

Task N: Explaining Choices, *continued*

Make a choice for each situation and explain why.

12. If I had to choose between working at night or during the day, I would choose _____

    because _____.

13. If I had to choose between babysitting for an infant or a three-year-old child, I would choose

    _____ because _____.

14. If I had to choose between living on a small island or living in a large city, I would choose

    _____ because _____.

15. If I had to choose between going surfing or snowboarding, I would choose _____

    because _____.

16. If I had to choose between staying home alone or going to a party where I didn't know a

    single person, I would choose _____ because _____.

17. If I had to choose between riding on a roller coaster or a merry-go-round, I would choose

    _____ because _____.

18. If I had to choose between working as a jockey or a racecar driver, I would choose

    _____ because _____.

19. If I had to choose between losing television privileges for a week or having extra chores for

    a week, I would choose _____ because _____

    _____.

20. If I had to choose between being the teacher or the principal of a school, I would choose

    _____ because _____.

21. If I had to choose between receiving a prize of fifty dollars or free movie passes for three

    months, I would choose _____ because _____

    _____.

22. If I had to choose between swimming in a lake or an ocean, I would choose _____

    because _____.

I.E.P. Objective: The client will choose between hypothetical situations and state a reason for each choice with 90% accuracy.

Task N: Explaining Choices, *continued*

Make a choice for each situation and explain why.

23. If I had to choose between having cable television or Internet service for my computer, I
     would choose _____ because _____

     _____ .

24. If I had to choose between being an actor/actress or a movie director, I would choose

     _____ because _____ .

25. If I had to choose between going to a rodeo or a stock car race, I would choose

     _____ because _____ .

26. If I had to choose between giving a speech in front of a large group or dancing alone on

     stage, I would choose _____ because _____

     _____ .

27. If I had to choose between getting a parking ticket or being late for an important meeting at

     work I would choose _____ because _____

     _____ .

28. If I had to choose between jumping from a bridge with a bungee cord or jumping from an

     airplane with a parachute, I would choose _____ because _____

     _____ .

29. If I could choose between traveling backward or forward in time, I would choose _____

     _____ because _____ .

30. If I had to choose between living in Asia or living in Africa, I would choose

     _____ because _____ .

31. If I had to choose between climbing Mt. Everest or exploring the wreckage of the *Titanic* in

     a submarine, I would choose _____ because _____

     _____ .

*I.E.P. Objective: The client will choose between hypothetical situations and state a reason for each choice with
        90% accuracy.*

Applying Language Skills
Task O: Choosing Names for Products

Choose the best name for each product. The first one is done for you.

1. sports car

   Mule   (Cheetah)   Opossum

2. hair conditioner that gets out all the tangles

   Terrible Tangler   Knots Out   All Tied Up

3. frozen pops with a hidden treat in each

   Fun-cicles   Power Pops   Vitasticks

4. floor cleaner

   Quick Slip   Mr. Grungy   Fine Shine

5. glue for children

   Toxic Hold   Quick Stick   Drip and Rip

6. television show for preschool children

   The Scare Chair   Teen Town   Cuddle Time

7. frozen energy shake

   Hot Stuff   Cool Fuel   Brain Freeze

8. breath-freshening dog bones

   Smoochie Poochies   Lazy Bones   Meow Lips

9. vacuum cleaner

   Grime Grabber   Dust Cloud   Dirt Flinger

10. small crackers for toddlers

    Baby Bites   Chili Squares   Spits Crackers

I.E.P. Objective: The client will choose fictitious names for products with 90% accuracy.

Task O: Choosing Names for Products, *continued*

Choose the best name for each product.

11. fur-lined slippers

    Frosty Footies   Toasty Toes   Dirty Dogs

12. window cleaner

    Shine 'n Sparkle   Streak 'n Smudge   Blue Haze

13. laundry detergent

    Almost Fresh   Power Out   Grime-in

14. sunscreen

    Intensifry   Shade and Shield   Sun Magnet

15. bottled water

    Creek Bottom   Aqualicious   Algae Blast

16. air freshener

    Garden Mist   Stink-Ups   Rot-and-Reek

17. motel

    Wake and Ache   Cloud Nine   The Pit Stop

18. gas station

    Fast Fill   Gas Is Us   The Oil Spill

19. bank

    Big Al's Bank   First Provident Bank The Money Pit

20. face lotion

    Wrinkle Up   Grimy Grit   Purely Radiant

I.E.P. Objective: The client will choose fictitious names for products with 90% accuracy.

Task O: Choosing Names for Products, *continued*

Choose the best name for each product.

21. salad dressing

    Fresh-a-licious   Soyglop   Dracula's Own

22. hot tub

    The Roaster   Soak 'n Sweat   The Soothing Spa

23. batteries

    NeverReady   Powerhouse   Dimlit

24. motor oil

    Gunk-Up   Glide and Ride   Sludgy

25. high school marching band

    The High Steppers   The Clodhoppers   The Accidents

26. magazine for teens

    Mother Goose's Garden   What Zup?   Travel Talk

27. running shoes

    Anchors   Sprints   Anvils

28. self-sharpening pencils

    Pen-tastics   Old Yellows   Eversharps

29. antiseptic cream that smells like lemons

    Lemon-Aid   Banana Heal   Germ-a-riffic

30. catch and release mousetraps

    Mice Cream   Trap-Free   Guilloteenies

I.E.P. Objective: The client will choose fictitious names for products with 90% accuracy.

Task P: Explaining Oxymorons

Oxymorons are two words used together that seem to have opposite meanings. Explain why each phrase below is an oxymoron. The first one is done for you.

1. We're out of popcorn. Pretzels are your **only choice**.

    If you have a choice, you have two or more items to select from. If there is only one item left, it is not a choice.

2. This is an **awfully good** movie.

    _____

3. **Jumbo shrimp** are on sale today at the market.

    _____

4. I heard about what happened at the game. That's **old news**.

    _____

5. My favorite candy is **red licorice**.

    _____

6. The clown gave us a **sad smile**.

    _____

7. These chairs have **hard cushions**.

    _____

8. What are you doing today? "**Nothing much**."

    _____

9. We heard a **loud whisper** from the back row.

    _____

10. I was so thirsty, I took a **big sip** of the hot chocolate.

    _____

11. That's a **pretty ugly** tale you are telling.

    _____

12. This is a **fine mess** we have gotten into!

    _____

13. If you cut the slice of cake, I get the **larger half**.

    _____

I.E.P. Objective: The client will explain oxymorons with 90% accuracy.

Task P: Explaining Oxymorons, *continued*

Explain why each phrase below is an oxymoron.

14. Joey is in the **advanced beginner** class.

_____

15. You must try our **new and improved** floor cleaner.

_____

16. The robbers set off the **silent alarm**.

_____

17. Let me just **think out loud** for a minute.

_____

18. Tie a **loose knot** in the rope at the stern.

_____

19. Gingersnaps are my **least favorite** cookie.

_____

20. The red paint bucket is **half empty**.

_____

21. Get out the **plastic glasses** to bring on the picnic.

_____

22. Now it's time to have some **serious fun**!

_____

23. Arlene is a **paid volunteer** at the science museum.

_____

24. The show is **taped live** each Tuesday.

_____

25. The **modern history** exam is tomorrow.

_____

26. Andrew gave an **accurate estimate** of the number of bricks he needed.

_____

I.E.P. Objective: The client will explain oxymorons with 90% accuracy.

146

Applying Language Skills
Task Q: Determining If Information Has Been Provided

I'll read a statement or question that asks for specific information. Listen carefully as I also read the response to the situation. Then say "Yes" or "No" to tell me if the response included the necessary information.

1. How long shall I stir the paint?

    "The last time I used it, I stirred it about a minute but it was still watery. The green paint doesn't need to be stirred as long as the blue paint."

2. Tell me how to get to your house.

    "Take Baker Street to 4th Avenue. Turn left. Go two blocks and turn right onto Cedar Street. We're the second house on the left."

3. How many children are coming to the party?

    "Nancy and her brother will be there. Three kids from school are coming and several kids from the neighborhood. If we count you and me, there will be 12 altogether. I hope we'll have enough food for everyone."

4. Who took the money off the table by the front door?

    "It was there when Lionel left for school. When I returned from the store, it was gone. Maybe Dad picked it up when he came back inside for his lunch pail. But he had money in his wallet. Perhaps Bart took it."

5. Will we be able to get the new bed up the stairs?

    "It's the same size as the bed we bought last year. We got that one upstairs without any difficulty so I'm sure we can get this one up too. Just be careful not to knock the pictures off the wall when you turn the corner."

6. How can you tell if the dishes in the dishwasher are clean?

    "This dishwasher is old, so sometimes the dishes look dirty even though they have been washed. You really can't tell just by looking at them. There is a better way to figure it out."

7. Have I missed the bus?

    "Well, it usually comes by 8:00. I got here a little before then but it wasn't here. Sometimes it is late, but not often. The next bus comes at 8:20, so if we see that one, we'll know we missed the first one."

8. I'm taking lunch orders. Please give me your order.

    "I might get the taco salad. I hope I have enough money for it. Let me check my wallet. What is everyone else getting? Does anyone want to split a pizza with me? Never mind. I had pizza last night for dinner."

I.E.P. Objective: The client will listen to explanations and determine if specified information has been provided with 90% or greater accuracy.

Task Q: Determining If Information Has Been Provided, *continued*

I'll read a statement or question that asks for specific information. Listen carefully as I also read the response to the situation. Then say "Yes" or "No" to tell me if the response included the necessary information.

9. Do you prefer to eat indoors or outside on the patio?

    "You know how allergic I am to bees. I'd better not take a chance and eat outside. But it has been such a rainy week up until now. I'm sure you'd rather eat outside and enjoy the sunshine. I'll just take my chances on the bees."

10. I need your name, address, phone number, and date of birth for this form.

    "You know my name. It's Kyle Webber. I was born on July 4, 1999. I live on Cedar Lane, and my phone number is 555-1212."

11. Tell me what days you are free this week.

    "This week is not too busy for me. I have to work on Monday and Wednesday, and I have a dentist appointment on Thursday morning. I'm not sure about Friday."

12. Do you have room for one more passenger in your car?

    "It all depends. The car seats four comfortably, but it's designed to hold five. I already promised Dan, Sandy, and Charles they could have a ride. If they don't bring a lot of baggage with them, we can probably take one more person. But if they have a lot of extra bags, we may not have room."

13. Explain how to fix this broken wire.

    "First, turn off the power. The electrical box is in the garage. Next, strip the insulation off the two ends of the wire where it has broken. Then use pliers to twist the ends of the wire together. Wrap several layers of electrical tape around this spot. Then turn the power back on to test the wire."

14. I don't remember how to play this card game. Do I deal each player five or seven cards to begin?

    "Did you look in the desk drawer for the directions? I thought I put them in there after we played the last time. But we've probably played it enough times that we don't need directions. You have to deal seven cards to each player and make two draw piles with the rest of the cards. Each player may play up to two cards on his turn."

15. Is this your backpack?

    "It looks like mine. It is the same color and brand. Look in the small pocket. If there is a yellow notebook inside, it is mine."

I.E.P. Objective: The client will listen to explanations and determine if specified information has been provided with 90% or greater accuracy.

Applying Language Skills
Task R: Determining When Information Has Been Provided

Listen as I read you a situation and the response to it. Say "Stop" when I've given you enough information to answer the question.

1. Did Mrs. Cobb assign any homework?

   "What do you think? Has there ever been a day when she did not give us homework? Of course she assigned us homework. We have to write a one-page story about a time when we were surprised. I'm going to write about that one time last month when she didn't give us homework. Boy, was I surprised! I'm sure I'll get an **A** on this assignment."

2. Is the Art Museum on this street?

   "The Art Museum is not far from here. I've been there many times. It's about three blocks down this street on the left. It's across the street from an old church. You can't miss it. It's a large building made of gray stone. There's a large sign in front that says 'Art Museum.'"

3. I'm allergic to strawberries. Are there any in this punch?

   "No. This punch contains orange juice, ginger ale, sugar, water, and pineapple juice. I'm also allergic to strawberries, so I read the list of ingredients carefully. If this punch contained strawberries, I would not drink it. It's fine for you to have some. I hope you like it."

4. I need help moving on Saturday. Can you help me move?

   "You're moving again? You just moved into this apartment last year. Don't you get tired of packing and moving? Have you even unpacked everything from the last time you moved? I shouldn't give you such a hard time. I'm just kidding. Of course I'll help you move on Saturday. I don't have any other plans."

5. What are you going to name your new puppy?

   "I thought about a lot of different names. I finally decided to name him Fred. Even though Fred is more of a person's name than a dog's name, I like it. My favorite uncle's name is Fred. He'll think it's funny that I'm naming my dog after him. My second choice was Snoopy, but there are a lot of dogs named Snoopy."

6. Will you scoot in your chair a little bit so I can get by?

   "Oh. I didn't realize I was blocking the aisle. This classroom is so small and they have too much furniture in here. It seems as if we are always tripping over one another. Of course I'll scoot in. There, can you make it by me now?"

7. When should we set the chairs out on the lawn?

   "It looks clear now, so I would go ahead and do it. If you wait until after lunch, it might be raining and you would get all wet. The chairs are plastic so it's okay if they get wet. We can just wipe them off with a rag before the ceremony begins. Thanks for your help."

I.E.P. Objective: The client will listen to explanations and determine when specified information has been provided with 90% or greater accuracy.

Task R: Determining When Information Has Been Provided, *continued*

Listen as I read you a situation and the response to it. Say "Stop" when I've given you enough information to answer the question.

8. Tell me where to put the toolbox.

"Oh, I didn't know you borrowed it. I was looking for it yesterday. It goes in the garage on the workbench. Did you borrow my saw too? I saw it last week, but now I can't find it."

9. Does everyone get the same size drink?

"I ordered large drinks for the adults and small drinks for the children. Some are lemonade and some are fruit punch. I didn't order any coffee or soda. I hope that's okay with everyone."

10. Why is it so windy today?

"I was wondering the same thing. It is so windy, our garbage can blew over and the shutters are rattling. I heard on the radio that there's a big storm off the coast. I guess it's causing all this windy weather."

11. I'm expecting a package from Lucy. Has the mail been delivered yet?

"I thought I heard the mail truck a few minutes ago. Look, the flag on the mailbox is down, so he must have come by already. I'll run out to the mailbox and see if your package is here. If it is, I'll bring it in."

12. I like this coat. Will it be going on sale soon?

"We just had a coat sale last week. Now they are back to the regular prices. It's too bad you didn't come in last week. Everything was on sale then. It's unlikely that coat will be on sale again within the next month."

13. Explain why you missed your curfew last night.

"My curfew is too early. No one else has to be home by ten o'clock. The movie didn't get out until 9:45, and by the time we got out of the parking lot and drove home, it was 10:15. I think I should have a later curfew. Will you please consider it?"

14. I thought I heard glass breaking. Is something wrong?

"No. Everything's okay. I dropped a glass in the sink when I was getting it out of the cupboard and it broke. But I cleaned it up and put the broken glass in the trash. Don't worry."

15. I just bought a new car for $35,000. Do you think I spent too much money?

"Well, I always buy used cars. I don't like to have huge car payments each month. I think anything over $25,000 is way too much to spend on a car. And, with a brand new car, you worry about it getting dented or stolen. But it's your money to do with as you like."

I.E.P. Objective: The client will listen to explanations and determine when specified information has been provided with 90% or greater accuracy.

Task R: Determining When Information Has Been Provided, *continued*

Listen as I read you a situation and the response to it. Say "Stop" when I've given you enough information to answer the question.

16. Are you related to Ellen Carter?

    "Her mother is my cousin. We don't see each other very often even though we are related. She works nights at the hospital, and I work days teaching school, so it is hard to schedule a visit. I like Ellen. It's too bad we don't see each other more often."

17. What is the name of Shiloh's veterinarian?

    "I don't remember. I always get it mixed up with the name of my dentist. My dentist's name is Dr. McMillan. I think the vet's name is Dr. Milliken. No, that's not it. The vet's name is Dr. McLean."

18. Why is there a live chicken in the dining room?

    "You won't believe what happened! I was sitting here watching TV. I heard the screech of brakes and then a loud crash. I opened the front door and ran outside. A truck carrying chickens had skidded around the corner and crashed into the tree beside our mailbox. Chickens were running everywhere! Once I saw that the driver was unhurt, I ran around chasing chickens, trying to get them back into their cages. You say there's a chicken in the dining room? I probably left the front door open, and it must have wandered inside and into the dining room. I'll go get it right now. What should I do with it?"

19. How can the gasoline can be empty? I just filled it yesterday.

    "This morning our next-door neighbor came over and said he had run out of gas while mowing his lawn. I told him he could use some of ours. I didn't realize he would use it all. I'll go down to the gas station right now and fill it back up. Is there anything else we need while I'm out? I should be back in about ten minutes."

20. What is the difference between a hurricane and a typhoon?

    "Both are violent storms that originate over water. Both a hurricane and a typhoon are dangerous. They cause serious damage to land and property and cost many lives. The main difference between a hurricane and a typhoon is that hurricanes begin in the Atlantic Ocean and typhoons begin in the Pacific Ocean, particulary in the China Sea."

21. Why should you wear sneakers or deck shoes in boats?

    "There are two reasons you should wear sneakers or deck shoes when boating. If you wear hard-soled shoes, you could damage the floor of the boat. Some people think that flip-flops would be good to wear because they don't get ruined if they are wet, but your feet can easily slide out of them and they offer no protection to your foot from a fishing hook. Sneakers and deck shoes have soft, rubber soles that provide traction on the wet surface of the boat deck. You won't be as likely to slip and fall, and they won't damage the boat."

I.E.P. Objective: The client will listen to explanations and determine when specified information has been provided with 90% or greater accuracy.

Answer Key

Suggested answers have been provided for most of the items. However, accept any reasonable responses your clients may give, as long as they back them up with appropriate reasoning.

Answering and Asking Questions
Task A   pages 7-8
2. baby
3. coach, captain
4. cowboy, cowgirl
5. nurse, doctor
6. acrobat, elephant, clown
7. president
8. police officer
9. babysitter
10. principal
11. astronaut
12. food server
13. safety patrol
14. detective
15. actor/actress, movie star
16. customer, shopper
17. neighbor
18. student
19. farmer
20. pioneers
21. passenger
22. fan
23. jogger
24. captain
25. cashier
26. audience
27. scuba diver
28. mother, girl
29. twin
30. senior
31. Girl Scout, Boy Scout
32. teenager
33. conductor
34. baker
35. magician
36. trucker
37. rapper
38. miner, geologist
39. governor
40. senator, representative

Task B   page 9
2. rabbit, frog, kangaroo
3. ball
4. tree
5. tiger, flag, zebra
6. clock
7. flower
8. boat

9. water
10. pants, jacket
11. dresser
12. water
13. yo-yo, top
14. bird
15. eyes, door, window
16. cat
17. car, bicycle
18. couch
19. egg
20. ruler, scale
21. plant, child
22. store, library
23. bus, theater
24. racetrack, highway
25. book
26. alarm clock, light
27. computer
28. foot, sock
29. medicine
30. ink, blood, grass
31. star
32. seed
33. rope
34. cloth, forehead
35. weather, traffic light
36. elevator, temperature, ocean
37. fish, doctor's office
38. coffee maker, fish tank
39. jacket
40. kitchen

Task C   pages 10-12
2. Your pants would get wet.
3. No one would be able to hear the movie.
4. All the water would run down the drain.
5. The food wouldn't cook.
6. People would have to carry their trash or the ground would be covered with trash.
7. The boat would probably tip over.
8. The batteries would die.
9. The teacher wouldn't know which paper belonged to which student.
10. You would smear ink on your paper when erasing.

11. It would be confusing when the teacher called on one of them.
12. She would choke on it or swallow it.
13. The chocolate would melt in the dryer and then stain the clothing.
14. Your food would be covered with too much salt.
15. Bugs would get in the house.
16. It would make footprints in the paint.
17. Riders would fall out.
18. The jelly would drip off in the toaster and burn.
19. The players would get very muddy as they played on a wet field.
20. nothing
21. The milk would sour.
22. They would freeze or be unable to find food under the snow.
23. People would need bigger mailboxes and have to wait longer to receive mail.
24. The alligators would eat the ducks.
25. The water would go right through the racket and the boat wouldn't move.
26. You would ride in circles.
27. The wood would smoke but it wouldn't burn.
28. Many people would be unable to buy shoes, or they would wear shoes that didn't fit.
29. Everyone could open everyone else's locker.
30. The tow truck would have to call a tow truck.
31. It would be difficult to store them or carry them when it was not raining.
32. Some students would not attend very often.
33. You would have to go to the store many times each week.
34. nothing
35. The stories would be hard to read and understand.

152

36. Fewer players would get on base and score runs.
37. The contact lens would disappear and perhaps melt.
38. Everyone would have to carry large coin purses to hold all of their money.
39. Drivers would have to stop suddenly without warning.

Task D   pages 13-15
2. use a friend's book
3. make half of a sandwich
4. use suspenders or a safety pin
5. feed it tuna fish or something else it likes
6. put your name on the waiting list
7. cut up a box
8. take some from another game
9. hang plastic over the window
10. bring it to the person later or go home and get it
11. call the store to see if the other shoe is there or return the shoe
12. leave a note explaining what happened
13. call for help
14. ask someone to go get it
15. fix something that doesn't need to be heated
16. dictate it to his parent or someone else
17. use the club to push it out
18. take the stairs
19. check the batteries
20. use a rope
21. use soap to make it slip off
22. unplug the phone or take it off the hook
23. ask the usher to bring a flashlight or wait until the movie is over
24. sit on the curb and massage it or stretch it out
25. open one to see what is in it and then rewrap it
26. cut the other side even with it
27. say "No thank you"
28. send it back to the kitchen
29. use another heavy object
30. use buttons or something else for the red checkers

31. move away from the leak or dry out the tent the next day
32. go to a neighbor's and call a family member to bring a key
33. take it to the bank and exchange it
34. ask a zoo worker to get it for you or leave it there
35. pick it up if it is floating or go without lunch
36. call someone to pick you up or hail a cab

Task E   pages 16-17
2. when the store is closing
3. when drinking
4. when I get my picture taken
5. when it is dropped
6. when someone rings it
7. after I get up
8. when it is stuck with a sharp object
9. when it rains and the sun is shining
10. when they play ring-around-the-rosy
11. before we start the car
12. when they want to answer a question or ask permission
13. during a slumber party
14. at dawn
15. when playing tag
16. at midnight on December 31
17. when the doctor looks at my throat
18. when a noise is too loud
19. in the fall
20. when we are cold
21. during a fire drill
22. in the winter
23. when they blow out birthday candles or throw pennies in fountains
24. during a storm or eclipse
25. early in the morning
26. when they are ready to fly, when they need food
27. when we have a rash, mosquito bites, or chickenpox
28. when we pledge allegiance
29. when there is an emergency
30. when I have given the cashier more money than the item costs
31. when it is ready to land

32. when there is a drought
33. when the batter has three strikes
34. when a team has made a touchdown
35. when it is returning to its home base
36. early in the morning or evening
37. when I have a cut
38. when it is snowing or raining
39. when I pass "Go"
40. when it is calm

Task F   pages 18-19
2. holidays, weekends, sometimes in the summer
3. when it is very high
4. during the day, when it is sunny
5. when she is sleepy, in the afternoon
6. when it is dried up
7. in the fall
8. when it is burnt out
9. when the electricity fails, when I am in the middle of the woods at night
10. when I am going uphill
11. on a windy day
12. when painting, camping, or working in the yard
13. when my old ones are too small or worn out
14. when I no longer hear the "pops"
15. when they have holes in them, when they are too small
16. when the cheese is melted and the crust is brown
17. at a matinee
18. when you want to find out what a word means or how to spell or pronounce it
19. when they are red and ripe
20. after a meal
21. when someone is sleeping, late at night
22. after the sun sets
23. when they are burnt
24. at noon
25. during or after a rainstorm while the sun is shining
26. when the peels are yellow and the fruit is soft
27. early in the morning, at dawn
28. in the winter

29. never
30. before the main attraction
31. at dusk, at sunset
32. when the last horse crosses the finish line
33. early in the morning
34. when mixing or removing food from a pan
35. when he is swinging, when his car is broken down
36. when the tank is on empty
37. on my birthday, specific date
38. July 4
39. in December, on the winter solstice
40. when it is sinking
41. when the door is closed
42. when the tread is worn

Task G   pages 20-21

2. when washing my hair
3. when someone is swinging
4. when I'm swimming or snorkeling
5. when they are flat
6. when driving, in class
7. when my pants are loose
8. when it is small
9. when it is icy
10. when they are ill, on holidays
11. when they are due
12. when it is on/still hot
13. when I go inside
14. right before dinner
15. right before I open it
16. when my old one is worn out
17. when I am on a picnic
18. when traffic is coming
19. when jumping from an airplane
20. when it is empty, when the milk is sour
21. in winter
22. when there is a stop sign, red light, or person or vehicle in its path
23. when I don't know how to spell/ pronounce a word, when I don't know what a word means
24. in school, at the dentist's office
25. when my clothing is on fire
26. when I don't know who is there, when my parents aren't home

27. when someone is sleeping, in class when others are working, when telling a secret
28. when I have the hiccups, when I'm underwater
29. when I can't find potholders, when it's not finished baking
30. the first day of the month
31. when something is coming toward my head
32. when it is addressed to someone else
33. when I am next to someone, when I am in a movie theater or library
34. after I have said goodbye
35. in an emergency when I need to get outside
36. when getting X-rayed, when hiding, when getting my photo taken
37. when writing a proper name or beginning a sentence
38. when there is a thunderstorm
39. when I must leave, when I have something very important to say
40. before I turn the computer off
41. anytime it is burning
42. when you're inside an airplane or building

Task H   pages 22-23

2. at the station, on the platform
3. in a palace, in a castle
4. in the freezer
5. at a restaurant
6. in the Arctic
7. on my lap
8. to the veterinarian
9. in the back
10. up in the air
11. in cocoons
12. in operating rooms
13. in its middle
14. at the end of a train
15. at a movie theater
16. underground
17. at a mall
18. in Washington, D.C., in the White House
19. at a motel or hotel
20. to the beach

21. in my chest
22. in the desert
23. on a football field
24. around the center of the Earth
25. a museum
26. at the bottom of the Atlantic Ocean
27. a volcano
28. in a pond
29. in a doctor's office/hospital
30. a farm
31. on a computer
32. at a wedding or prom
33. at a car race
34. in an engine, parts store, or repair shop
35. in a hangar
36. at a bookstore or farm supply store
37. in a bank
38. to a zoo
39. in an oyster
40. at the center of the target
41. in England and other countries
42. hospitals, doctor's offices

Task I   pages 24-25

2. ketchup
3. notebook paper
4. playing Ping-Pong
5. van
6. scooter
7. pies
8. sandwiches
9. school lunch
10. soccer
11. wooden box
12. raisins
13. donkey
14. boots
15. hanging up my jacket
16. rabbit
17. hammock
18. noon
19. pliers
20. raisins
21. reef
22. calculator
23. aquarium
24. in a tree
25. climb a rope
26. pumpkins on the vine
27. football

28. tennis ball
29. violin
30. lullaby
31. helicopter
32. Hurricanes
33. plant
34. stadium
35. rowing
36. Mary Poppins
37. wood
38. bottom floor
39. teacher
40. match

Task J   pages 26-28
2. because the peel is too tough to chew
3. to pull on to open the drawers
4. to help drivers stay on their side of the road
5. to help it hold onto branches
6. to filter the bright light
7. so they don't dry out
8. so you don't burn your hands
9. to keep them from breaking
10. so you can see who is at the door before opening it
11. to display the country and state flags
12. to reach upper floors of tall buildings
13. so it can be returned to you if it can't be delivered
14. because the movies are sad
15. to help them stay on the horse, because it is more comfortable
16. to warn anyone behind them
17. to help people get up and down them quickly
18. because they fall often and the ice is hard
19. so we can carry them without water splashing on us
20. so children can't open them
21. so the cake won't stick to the pan when we take it out
22. to keep thieves from stealing artwork and to keep visitors from touching it
23. so the driver can see what is coming up beside him
24. to make money to pay for the programs

25. to break up hard soil for digging
26. to store fat to use as food
27. to adjust them for different-sized waists
28. to provide privacy for the passengers
29. so we can easily reach the person we want to speak to
30. so all your cards look alike to your opponents
31. so only you can withdraw your money
32. to avoid spreading illness
33. to make it easier for the seeds to sprout and grow
34. to save resources and energy
35. so the gas doesn't catch on fire
36. for Daylight Saving Time
37. to show respect for the flag
38. because it is their home
39. so that only a small amount of sand can go through at any time

Task K   pages 29-31
2. because there is not enough room
3. because it is not comfortable
4. because it is too hot
5. because the water would burn our hands
6. because it will spoil if it is not kept cold
7. because it is distracting and messy
8. because the lightbulb is hot
9. because it is difficult to roller-skate on carpet
10. because it would hurt if someone fell on them
11. because the runner could slip and fall
12. because they are too young and not responsible enough
13. because we would pass germs and illnesses to one another
14. because they might spill food on the merchandise
15. because it might rain, someone might steal the car
16. because it is hard to eat that many scoops before they melt, more than three scoops will fall off easily

17. because it is harder to see the movie when the lights are on
18. because they aren't ripe until fall
19. because the cleats would ruin the gym floor
20. because they can't carry their instruments
21. because a rake can't move the snow
22. because they can't open the door, because they might run away
23. because turkeys can't fly
24. because we might be too full to eat our meal
25. because their lawns are covered with snow
26. because it is not an emergency
27. because it is illegal
28. because it is too dangerous
29. because stones are too heavy to carry in the beaks, because stones would make a heavy/hard nest
30. because it is powered by the wind and doesn't need a motor
31. because it would take too long to reach its destination, there might not be a train station in each town
32. because their metal clubs might cause them to be struck by lightning
33. because the fire could short out the wires and they would be trapped
34. because it will take the blue color out
35. because it is dangerous, fish feed at night
36. because they don't live in water
37. because they are too heavy to climb steep mountains
38. because large leaves require a lot of water and the desert is very dry
39. because criminals could open them and jump out

Task L   pages 32-33
2. quiet
3. cold
4. sweet

Answer Key, *continued*

5. sharp
6. slowly
7. scary
8. sticky
9. loud
10. stinky, bad
11. warm
12. dirty
13. funny, silly
14. heavy, smooth
15. messy
16. tired
17. lucky, glad
18. wrinkled, crumpled
19. crunchy, noisy
20. rough
21. sour
22. hot
23. salty
24. good, delicious
25. lonely, sad
26. scaly, cool
27. beautiful
28. disappointed, mad
29. sore, tired
30. proud, happy
31. slimy, gooey
32. sparkly, shiny
33. foggy
34. empty
35. smooth
36. bright
37. fast
38. tall
39. thirsty, dusty
40. dry

Task M   pages 34-36
2. The grass and road are wet.
3. They smell bad or look dirty.
4. It is hard.
5. You have a substitute teacher.
6. It beeps.
7. The grass is long.
8. The gauge is on E, The car stops going.
9. The can is empty.
10. The person who answers the phone tells you.
11. You can see dirt on it.
12. It isn't cold, Everything in the freezer has melted.
13. Look at the date stamp.

14. He measures himself, His pants are too short, He can reach a higher shelf.
15. Their car is gone, There are newspapers in the driveway.
16. It is black, You can smell it burning.
17. You hear music/bells.
18. The flag on the mailbox is down, There is new mail in the mailbox.
19. All the pins are down.
20. It has disappeared, The juice tastes watery.
21. The bathroom is steamy.
22. It loses air and becomes flat.
23. Everyone has started eating.
24. They look clean, They're not stretched out.
25. It has no leaves, It falls down.
26. It shows the same time whenever you check it.
27. There is an announcement on TV or on the radio.
28. There are car seats in the backseat, There are toys on the floor of the car.
29. You have a fever or sore throat.
30. The thunder is loud, You see lightning near you.
31. The tip is black.
32. The nest is empty, You find empty shells.
33. You see the names at the end, The lights in the theater come on.
34. You look at a calendar, You see flowers starting to bloom.
35. They won't cut paper.
36. You look at the date, The paper is much bigger, There are many advertisement pages.
37. Cars are backed up, Cars stop in all directions.
38. They make an announcement, They lock the doors.
39. Lines are stamped through it.

Task N   pages 37-38
2. yes
3. yes
4. no
5. no
6. yes
7. yes
8. yes
9. no
10. no
11. no
12. no
13. no
14. no
15. yes
16. no
17. no
18. no
19. no
20. yes
21. yes
22. no
23. no
24. yes
25. no
26. yes
27. no
28. yes
29. no
30. yes
31. yes
32. no
33. no
34. yes
35. no
36. no
37. yes
38. yes
39. no
40. yes

Task O   pages 39-40
2. false; It will boil.
3. false; A car has more horsepower and can go faster.
4. true
5. true
6. false; Daisies have smooth stems.
7. true
8. false; Visors don't have a top.
9. false; They are soggy.
10. false; You or your dog could get hit by a car.
11. false; Spiders live on webs.
12. true
13. true
14. true
15. true
16. false; It is a model of the Earth.
17. false; They should stop before they reach the tracks.
18. false; You run to first base after you hit the ball.
19. true
20. true
21. true
22. true
23. false; A young duck is called a duckling.
24. false; You can use them indoors too.
25. true
26. false; It has one less side than a rectangle.
27. false; Nine is an odd number and can't be divided evenly.
28. true
29. true

Answer Key, *continued*

30. false; A baby polar bear is called a cub.
31. true
32. true
33. false; *Permanent* means *everlasting*.
34. false; Wet towels are heavier because they hold water.
35. true
36. false; We read from left to right.
37. true
38. false; There are three colors.
39. false; Gold is worth more than silver.
40. true

Task P   pages 41-42
Answers will vary.

Describing Objects and Defining Words
Task A   pages 43-44
2. drink it, water a plant
3. play tug of war, tie knots
4. make a campfire, throw it to the dog
5. bounce it, kick it
6. put groceries in it, make a mask from it
7. ride in it, use it to deliver papers
8. mail something, keep puppies in it
9. hang up wet clothing, close snack bags
10. chop down tree, cut firewood
11. close a package, fix a rip in paper
12. eat it, make a jack-o'-lantern
13. pour milk from it, make a bird feeder
14. put sandwich in it, keep coins in it
15. sleep under it, make a fort
16. sit on it, put clothes on it
17. shoot it, wrap it around a newspaper
18. read it, cut out pictures
19. put it in a vase, smell it
20. fry it, make a cake
21. dry hands, clean up a mess
22. put it in hair, tie it around a package
23. measure, draw a straight line

24. spin it around your waist, jump through it
25. catch a butterfly, hit a ball over it
26. buy something, throw it in a fountain
27. drink through it, blow paint with it
28. plant something in it, put it on a desk to keep pencils in
29. build a wall, use it as a doorstop
30. wipe off table, paint with it
31. read it, wrap up something in it
32. make applesauce, make a pie
33. mail a letter, keep small things in it
34. wrap food in it, make a decoration
35. tighten a screw, scrape paint off something
36. wear it on your head, tie it over your nose/mouth to keep out dust
37. wear it, make a puppet
38. eat it, put it in soup
39. knit a sweater, make a doll
40. burn it, use it to build something
41. salute it, wave it
42. look up a definition, press leaves in it

Task B   page 45
2. soda, juice
3. button, marble
4. elephant, gorilla
5. kitten, bunny
6. ice cream, snow
7. cloud, cave
8. sun, school bus
9. apple, stoplight
10. forest, stormy night
11. apple, pear
12. ketchup, juice
13. beach ball, balloon
14. dime, ring
15. sword, stick
16. sponge, feather
17. truck, airplane
18. pea, apple
19. chili pepper, flame
20. sheep
21. rainbow, flower
22. cotton candy

23. glass, window
24. knife, scissors
25. waterslide, seal
26. socks
27. ice cube, icicle
28. raincoat
29. river
30. pinecone
31. jeans
32. pickle, candy
33. coffee, tea
34. oatmeal
35. chocolate
36. mosquito, gnat
37. French fries
38. rose
39. swimming pool water
40. test, marathon

Task C   pages 46-47
2. cut
3. shine
4. ring
5. pop
6. roll
7. soak up water
8. talk, fly
9. keep water out of eyes
10. spin
11. moo, give milk
12. fly
13. hop
14. roll
15. keep papers from blowing away
16. hold a dog
17. keep your hands warm
18. take people up and down in a building
19. protect your foot
20. hold clothes, bread, etc.
21. keep a wound clean
22. chop wood
23. protect your head
24. chop food
25. stretch
26. attach things
27. warn ships
28. hold up a swing
29. dig up a field
30. save you money
31. keep out light
32. take temperature
33. help someone walk

34. keep you from getting a sunburn
35. keep you healthy
36. kill germs
37. turn, make power
38. move the cursor
39. power a car
40. hold an object to a hard surface
41. move things from one place to another
42. make electricity

Task D   page 48

2. true	22. false
3. false	23. false
4. true	24. false
5. true	25. true
6. false	26. false
7. true	27. true
8. false	28. true
9. false	29. false
10. false	30. true
11. true	31. true
12. true	32. true
13. true	33. false
14. false	34. true
15. true	35. true
16. true	36. true
17. false	37. false
18. false	38. true
19. true	39. false
20. true	40. true
21. false	

Task E   pages 49-50

2. tweet
3. beep
4. shout
5. mark
6. sketch
7. whistle
8. chop
9. blink
10. bark
11. neigh
12. rise
13. bounce
14. scream
15. pack
16. print
17. gallop
18. march
19. trim
20. rinse

21. cheer
22. add
23. skip
24. creep
25. punch
26. climb
27. chirp
28. giggle
29. fold
30. stew
31. yell
32. sleep
33. reach
34. hope
35. curl
36. enclose
37. trot
38. disinfect
39. scamper
40. bend
41. churn
42. repeat

Task F   pages 51-52

2. swim
3. fly
4. moo
5. hop
6. crawl
7. slither
8. growl
9. swim
10. spin
11. leap
12. walk
13. see
14. drip
15. wiggle
16. speak
17-42. Answers will vary.

Task G   pages 53-54
Answers will vary.

Task H   pages 55-57

2. Both are fruits, but apples are red, green, or yellow and peaches are orange.
3. Both are birds, but a duck quacks and a turkey gobbles.
4. Both are round or square snack foods, but cookies taste sweet and crackers taste salty.
5. Both have nails, but fingers are on our hands and toes are on our feet.
6. Both tell time, but a clock hangs on the wall and a watch is usually worn on a person's wrist.
7. Both are containers, but a bucket has a handle and a bowl does not.
8. Both are eating utensils, but a spoon is rounded and a fork is pointed.
9. People wear both on their feet, but they wear shoes outdoors and slippers indoors.
10. People ride both in the water, but a surfboard is powered by waves and a saiboat is powered by the wind or a motor.
11. Both are tools with long handles, but we use a rake for gathering leaves and a broom for sweeping dirt.
12. Both are small, furry animals, but a gerbil can be a pet and a chipmunk lives in the wild.
13. Both are cold, sweet treats, but a snow cone is made of ice and an ice-cream cone is made of frozen cream.
14. Both are homes for groups of insects, but a beehive is made of honeycomb and an anthill is made of dirt.
15. Both are bodies of water, but a lake is surrounded by land and an ocean isn't.
16. Both are sources of entertainment/information, but you only listen to a radio and you listen to and watch a TV.
17. We see both in the sky at night, but the moon looks different each night and stars appear as fixed points of light.
18. Both are four-legged animals with manes and tails, but zebras' coats are black and white striped and horses' coats can be brown, black, gray, or white.
19. Both are programs for young children, but children are 5 or

Answer Key, *continued*

6 in kindergarten and they are younger than that in preschool.

20. Both are places to swim, but a swimming pool has concrete on the bottom and a pond has mud on the bottom.

21. Both are amusement park rides, but a Ferris wheel moves vertically and a merry-go-round moves horizontally.

22. Both magnify objects, but we use a telescope for looking at objects in space and binoculars for looking at things in our environment.

23. Both are stringed instruments, but you use your hands to play a guitar and a bow to play a violin.

24. Both provide geographical information, but a map is a flat diagram and a globe is a three-dimensional model.

25. People wear both on their heads, but a baseball cap has a bill in the front and a cowboy hat has a brim all the way around it.

26. Both are tools with two handles, but we use scissors for cutting and pliers for grasping and twisting.

27. Both are buildings with many rooms, but a hospital is where people care for patients and a school is where people teach students.

28. Both have rounded tops and are made of cloth, but people use a parachute when jumping from an airplane and an umbrella when it rains.

29. People use both to communicate verbally, but a walkie-talkie can only transmit messages over short distances and a telephone can transmit messages over longer distances.

30. Both give news and information, but most newspapers are published daily and most magazines are published monthly.

31. Both are small, metal objects we use to fasten papers, but a paperclip is fastened around the papers and a staple is punched through the papers.

32. Both are body parts attached to the sides of the body, but a wing is part of an insect or bird and an arm is part of a person or ape.

33. Both provide factual information, but a dictionary gives definitions and pronunciations and an encyclopedia gives detailed information on a topic.

34. Both are large creatures with four legs and long tails, but dragons are make-believe and dinosaurs were alive at one time.

35. Both are superheroes that help people in trouble, but Spiderman moves by shooting webs at buildings and Superman flies through the air.

36. Both are stories, usually make-believe, but a dream occurs in your mind and a movie is shown on a screen.

Task I   pages 58-59

2. twins
3. yawn
4. wag
5. French fries
6. toast
7. shell
8. quiz
9. bib
10. sweep
11. pole
12. juice
13. awake
14. pasture
15. green
16. liquid
17. bank
18. cousin
19. hood
20. sidewalk
21. stir
22. loaf
23. calendar
24. helmet
25. quilt

26. exit
27. map
28. puddle
29. scale
30. garage
31. spell
32. ankle
33. pocket
34. graduation
35. remote control
36. prey
37. scar
38. charge
39. jockey
40. kaleidoscope
41. exercise

Task J   pages 60-61

2. animals, things to ride
3. wooden things, writing tools
4. toys, furry things
5. containers, things with a zipper
6. things that fly, vehicles
7. footwear, cowboy equipment
8. sea animals, food
9. colorful objects, things that spin
10. vehicles, noisy things
11. sharp objects, things made of metal
12. sweet things, sticky things
13. things that are white, snack foods, salty things
14. things with a cover, things you can read
15. things that are soft, rectangular things
16. cold things, things that are very small
17. birds, night animals
18. things made of paper, things with numerals on them
19. things that ring, things made of plastic
20. sweet things, frozen things
21. dark places, animal homes
22. small things, things made of metal
23. clothing, things you wear on your head
24. frozen things, hard things
25. things with handles, places to keep money

Answer Key, *continued*

26. things that are dusty, things you write with
27. things with holes, sandwich ingredients
28. liquids, medicine
29. vehicles, things on a farm
30. green things, soft things
31. clothing, things that are waterproof
32. things made of leather, things that hold money
33. things with glass, rectangular objects
34. things that are cube-shaped, things with spots
35. things that whistle, things you would find in the kitchen
36. things you can sleep on, things with springs
37. hollow things, light things
38. things that are long, things that come in pairs
39. wooden things, containers
40. liquids, fuel
41. sea animals, things with many arms
42. things with leaves, things that make you itch

Task K   pages 62-63
2. oink
3. asleep
4. feathers
5. marks
6. girl
7. summer
8. cools
9. babies
10. paws
11. cow, elephant, whale
12. seeds
13. knees
14. chicken
15. cereal
16. licking
17. round
18. bricks
19. solid
20. Valentine's Day
21. books
22. blankets
23. strings
24. runs
25. shells

26. even
27. instruments
28. letters
29. bills, money
30. hoot
31. slither
32. vine
33. sour
34. tickets
35. bulletin board
36. dams
37. recess, snack time
38. chest
39. governor
40. Paris, France
41. *three*
42. person

Task L   pages 64-65
2. orange
3. wrist
4. swim
5. happy
6. hive
7. cake
8. book
9. fork, spoon
10. lips
11. ears
12. camel, lizard
13. bird
14. low
15. bed
16. football
17. four
18. dog, cat
19. chew
20. stick
21. nail
22. knot
23. tree
24. rope, pogo stick
25. dance, twirl
26. ant
27. paw
28. core
29. doughnut
30. second
31. temperature
32. car
33. no
34. eye
35. river
36. parking lot

37. Japanese
38. England
39. Hawaii
40. South America

Task M   pages 66-67
2. sea animals, have claws
3. baby animals, soft
4. black, fly
5. large animals, grey
6. places to swim, have fish
7. vegetables, grow underground
8. jewelry, round
9. round, used to play games
10. used to hold things, have wheels
11. long sticks, used to hit an object
12. made of cloth, rectangular
13. sweet, sticky
14. vehicles, go in air
15. write with them, long and thin
16. sticky on back, pictures on front
17. toys, on strings
18. keep us warm, wear on top part of body
19. sweet, chewy
20. musical instruments, have keys
21. vegetables, green
22. noisy, are pushed
23. two wheels, ride them
24. yellow, spread on bread
25. flat, ride on them
26. live in water, have sharp teeth
27. sharp, used when sewing
28. in amusement park, have steep inclines
29. hard, grow on trees
30. sports arenas, places with bleachers
31. have actors, entertainment
32. hot foods, eaten with spoon
33. can draw or write on, easily erased
34. athletic equipment, can jump on
35. go around a yard, used for privacy
36. round with hole in middle, filled with air
37. thick books, in alphabetical order
38. have numerical keys, need batteries
39. magnify objects, used in science
40. mythical creatures, four-legged animals

Answer Key, *continued*

41. make holes in wood, noisy
42. have holes in the middle, put in mouth

Task N   pages 68-71
2. athletic
3. spoiled
4. dreary
5. ripe
6. drowsy
7. fancy
8. responsible
9. greedy
10. messy
11. valuable
12. thrifty
13. boring
14. stubborn
15. frisky
16. gentle
17. confused
18. annoying
19. weary
20. blank
21. courteous
22. nervous
23. jealous
24. impatient
25. embarrassed
26. hazy
27. discouraged
28. ambitious
29. optimistic
30. victorious
31. agonizing
32. reassuring

Task O   pages 72-73
2. held tightly
3. burning
4. bends easily
5. smooth
6. job
7. cloudy
8. living in the ocean
9. a storage cupboard for food
10. money
11. to carve wood
12. one-of-a-kind
13. applause
14. thick
15. sad
16. promise

17. introduced from another country
18. bump
19. moderately warm
20. permission
21. edge, border
22. habit
23. convince
24. symbol
25. a valley with steep sides
26. understand
27. the middle region of the torso
28. appearing at night
29. whole, unbroken

Reading and Listening
Task A   pages 74-76

1. b		13. a
2. c		14. b
3. b		15. c
4. c		16. a
5. a		17. a
6. b		18. c
7. c		19. a
8. b		20. b
9. a		21. b
10. c		22. a
11. b		23. c
12. c		24. a

Task B   pages 77-81

1. b		10. a
2. c		11. c
3. b		12. b
4. c		13. c
5. a		14. c
6. c		15. b
7. a		16. a
8. b		17. b
9. a		

Task C   pages 82-84
Answers will vary.

Task D   pages 85-90
1a. so no one would hear him
  b. in a tree
  c. leafy perch, shoe fell to the ground
  d. nighttime
  e. It fell off when he moved.
  f. no
  g. I found you!

  h. hide-and-seek
  i. scary to fun
  j. Answers will vary.

2a. early elementary age, riding your tricycle
  b. no
  c. confident
  d. nervous
  e. bicycle helmet
  f. Kyle had gotten hit
  g. She was scared.
  h. relieved, happy
  i. She was glad he didn't get hurt.
  j. Answers will vary.

3a. stay up late at night studying, He has an algebra final the next day.
  b. no
  c. because he had been studying algebra before he fell asleep
  d. sleet, hail
  e. He didn't want to take the final.
  f. excited, relieved
  g. to see if school had been cancelled
  h. He wouldn't have to take the final today.
  i. high school, algebra final and Heritage High
  j. Answers will vary.

4a. out West in the 1800s
  b. no
  c. to help Carol
  d. the current was too strong
  e. so it would be easier to swim
  f. The wagon she was riding in tipped over and she fell in.
  g. Mrs. Olson is Carol's mother.
  h. Jack is the movie director, and Brad and Courtney are the actors.
  i. the last paragraph
  j. Answers will vary.

5a. painter, He's on a ladder with a paintbrush.
  b. back of someone's home, backyard

c. He's been a painter for 20 years, mid-forties
d. so he can climb down to the ground
e. It's too far.
f. He's about to fall at any moment.
g. He wasn't as high on the ladder yesterday.
h. positive
i. The boy might go get help.
j. Answers will vary.

6a. airplane, gazed out city lights through the clouds, baggage claim area
b. They're sisters.
c. her son, Danny
d. They live far away from each other.
e. He had on dark glasses and a dark coat.
f. a rubber duckie and a stuffed bunny
g. She had his suitcase.
h. checked the tag on the suitcase before taking it out of the baggage claim area
i. It might have a tag on it that tells how to contact the owner.
j. Answers will vary.

7a. in a clothing store when it first opens in the morning
b. He was the last employee to leave the store.
c. He wouldn't bother for such a small amount of money. He would keep it.
d. It was a way to make people think he was honest.
e. She thinks he ran off with the money and isn't coming back to work.
f. She thinks he's honest.
g. He stopped at the bank to get change.
h. She jumps to conclusions. She is critical.
i. She felt bad that she had accused him of stealing.
j. Answers will vary.

8a. bad thunderstorm or hurricane; strong wind and rain, broken tree branches, lost electricity, damage to garage and vehicle
b. nighttime
c. watching the storm to see where it would go next
d. They knew the storm was coming.
e. A downed power line that still has electricity running through it may wiggle and bounce on the ground, making it look like it's dancing.
f. go near the downed power line
g. Emergency vehicles were going to help someone.
h. Stella is okay.
i. started cleaning up around their home
j. Answers will vary.

Task E   pages 91-95
1a. dog; vet, chasing cars
b. by what he says and how he says it
c. He said it was okay, it could have happened to anyone.
d. Answers will vary.
e. Answers will vary.
f. Answers will vary.

2a. at a restaurant, food servers
b. I'll take care of it.
c. I'm sorry.
d. Answers will vary.
e. Answers will vary.
f. Answers will vary.

3a. playing miniature golf
b. no, He said his friends talked him into playing because they needed another person.
c. no, only 3 players' names are given; they have a foursome
d. his golf club
e. complaining
f. Answers will vary.

4a. It's raining very hard.
b. herself

c. probably an adult, taking the bus to work
d. trying not to step in puddles, so her feet wouldn't get wet
e. Her umbrella is getting caught in the wind, making it look as if she's about to take off into the air like Mary Poppins.
f. Answers will vary.

5a. She thought the truck might have caused the house to shake.
b. Dana's room is at the front of the house, and her brother's room is at the back of the house.
c. an earthquake
d. It had fallen onto the floor.
e. because they live two miles from each other and still felt the same thing
f. Answers will vary.

6a. school; bell rang, children in hallway, classroom
b. a test or quiz
c. She was embarrassed or disappointed.
d. The test was easy.
e. There was a problem with Maria's test.
f. Answers will vary.

7a. No more food will grow until the weather gets warmer.
b. squirrel, chipmunk; The family lives in a burrow and can climb trees.
c. no
d. The children weren't smiling anymore.
e. winter
f. Answers will vary.

8a. husband and wife
b. watching Mrs. Carter run after Adam so she can give him whatever he forgot that morning
c. previous experience
d. John and Hilda's son
e. Answers will vary.

f. whether Mrs. Carter ever caught up with Adam and gave him his lunch bag

9a. fitness center, He's exercising in a building where other people are.
b. walking on a treadmill
c. He fell down.
d. because he bumped it on the floor when he fell, because he fell down
e. a worker at the fitness center, because the treadmill is broken
f. Answers will vary.

10a. They're collecting food from people's homes.
b. They're trying to collect more food than any other troop.
c. Cub Scouts or Boy Scouts
d. a food bank
e. Answers will vary.
f. Answers will vary.

Task F   pages 96-101
Answers will vary.

Applying Language Skills
Task A   pages 102-104
Answers will vary.

Task B   pages 105-107
2. It's time for you to go home.
3. I would like a drink.
4. Help me carry the groceries.
5. I'd like some popcorn.
6. Why don't you turn on the light?
7. Did you eat my candy bar?
8. Kevin, stop kicking the back of my chair.
9. You need to be quiet and let someone else speak.
10. Jerry, stop eating all the cookies.
11. Pick up the papers so I can vacuum your room.
12. Did you take my pen?
13. I'd like a strawberry.
14. Don't lose the key.
15. You'd better pick up that toy.
16. You should give your horse some water.

17. Everyone needs to be quiet and listen.
18. Your car is very dirty.
19. Let's go a little later.
20. You look tired today.
21. I expected you to call me and you didn't.
22. Are you being honest about your score?
23. It tastes sour. I need some sugar.
24. Sandra is bossy.
25. I don't want to invite Ella.
26. I didn't care for the play.
27. I'm tired of being in charge.
28. Can you lower the price of the car?
29. I want to go to a movie with my friends on Saturday.
30. You took my seat when I got up.
31. I heard your dog barking all night!
32. You were late for work today.
33. Why wasn't I invited to the party?
34. I'd like to go out with your cousin.
35. We'd like to try out your new hot tub.
36. You are very critical of my work.
37. Use the front door. I don't want you to get the kitchen floor dirty.
38. May I keep the change?
39. You called too early and woke me up!

Task C   pages 108-109
2. no answer
3. answer
4. answer
5. no answer
6. no answer
7. answer
8. no answer
9. answer
10. no answer
11. answer
12. no answer
13. no answer
14. answer
15. no answer
16. answer
17. no answer
18. no answer

19. answer
20. no answer
21. no answer
22. answer
23. answer
24. no answer
25. no answer
26. answer
27. no answer
28. answer
29. no answer
30. answer
31. no answer
32. no answer
33. no answer
34. answer
35. answer
36. no answer
37. answer
38. answer
39. no answer
40. answer
41. no answer
42. no answer

Task D   pages 110-112
Answers will vary.

Task E   pages 113-115
Answers will vary.

Task F   pages 116-118

2. b	14. b
3. c	15. a
4. a	16. b
5. c	17. a
6. c	18. c
7. a	19. a
8. a	20. b
9. c	21. a
10. b	22. b
11. b	23. a
12. c	24. c
13. c	

Task G   pages 119-121
2. apples and oranges
It's comparing two things that aren't alike.
3. good and ready
I won't do it until I want to.
4. black and white
I want to see it in writing.

163

Answer Key, *continued*

5. one and only
Carol is the famous spelling bee winner!

6. plain and simple
You can't ignore the absolute truth.

7. alive and kicking
The Hornets are strong and ready to play!

8. touch and go
For a while, it seemed like Stanley might die.

9. quick and dirty
Let's review the chapter quickly, without much discussion.

10. give and take
Everyone must compromise if we want to get along.

11. free and easy
In the summertime, everything is relaxed.

12. p's and q's
Be on your good behavior while Grandma is here.

13. high and dry
If you borrow the car, I won't have any transportation.

14. down and out
If I don't find a job, I'll have no way to support myself.

15. short and sweet
The graduation speech did not go on too long.

16. grin and bear it
I know it's hot, but try to make the best of the situation.

17. neck and neck
When the horses rounded the turn, they were exactly even.

18. tried and true
I may be old-fashioned, but my way is proven to work.

19. open-and-shut
My lawyer says there is nothing to debate about this case.

20. thick and thin
A true friend will stick by you in good times and bad.

21. cash and carry
You must pay cash for everything at the flea market and take your purchases with you.

Task H   pages 122-125

2. home; Home is the best place to be.
3. sky's; There is no limit.
4. blink; They disappeared quickly.
5. worm; The first person to arrive gets the best things.
6. want; If you use resources wisely, you will have more.
7. win; You can't win every time.
8. waste; When you hurry, you make mistakes.
9. Beggars; When asking for something, you have to take what you are offered.
10. never; It's better to come late than not come at all.
11. cat; When the person in charge is gone, people don't work as hard.
12. pain; You can't achieve something without hard work.
13. chew; Don't take on too much responsibility.
14. work; Every day, things happen that we may not like.
15. everyone; No matter what you do, someone is not going to like it.
16. stand; We are stronger if we join together.
17. sink; Only one person should be in charge.
18. never; Don't say you will never do something.
19. day; Get everything you can out of each day.
20. one; A person criticizing another is often guilty of the same behavior.
21. small; Ignore small matters or annoyances.
22. right; You can't undo a mistake by doing something else dishonest or incorrect.
23. mouth; Don't be critical of something you've been given.
24. cooks; When too many people are involved in something, it can go wrong.
25. cover; Judge a person by how he acts rather than how he looks.

26. Beauty; Just because someone looks nice doesn't mean the person is nice.
27. eat; If you eat a healthy/ unhealthy diet, you will be healthy/unhealthy.
28. cloud; Something good can be found in bad situations.

Task I   pages 126-128

2. glass
3. ice
4. cardboard
5. fish
6. feather
7. tack
8. cotton
9. knife
10. dream
11. cat up a tree
12. nails
13. whistle
14. hills
15. wink
16. canary
17. kitten
18. fiddle
19. ox
20. deer
21. rag doll
22. eagle
23. horse
24. mud
25. baby
26. carpet
27. fleas
28. sharks
29. trap door
30. frozen waterfall

Task J   pages 129-130

2. ox
3. feather
4. leather
5. wind
6. ice
7. bird
8. freight train
9. mountains, hills
10. pie
11. lion
12. mud

Answer Key, *continued*

13. dog
14. pig
15. mice
16. ocean
17. rocks
18. tacks
19. hornet
20. bee
21. wolves
22. prunes
23. rock
24. clown
25. silk
26. grass
27. a lemon
28. ant
29. trees
30. statue
31. toothpicks
32. oven
33. button, kitten, bug
34. clam
35. picture
36. leprechaun
37. sea, ocean, sky
38. load of bricks
39. bear
40. pancake
41. wolf, bear
42. lamb

Task K   pages 131-133
2. Her room is very messy.
3. Jill likes to joke around.
4. My feet are very cold.
5. David knows a lot of facts about a lot of things.
6. The brain holds many different things to help you solve problems.
7. Grandma's garden is full of beautiful colors.
8. Her smile really cheers me up.
9. Children are very receptive to new thoughts and ideas.
10. The puppies are very funny.
11. This car is very old.
12. Our classroom is chaotic.
13. Kelly's hair is a mess in the mornings.
14. The children were excited to get ice cream from the ice-cream truck.

15. A good teacher is in control of the situation.
16. Cara has lots of new, fresh ideas.
17. A new baby is something precious for the parents to treasure.
18. That horse is very skinny.
19. Laughter will make you feel better.
20. The twins are alike in many ways.
21. Use your time wisely. It is valuable.
22. The grass and bushes in our backyard need cutting.
23. I was happy to hear the car in our driveway.
24. Every day brings new things.
25. I am upset by the overdue bill.
26. Tyra seems to have a lot of bad luck.
27. Beagles like to romp and play.
28. His grandson's visit really cheered him up.
29. Spring is when all the flowers and trees begin to bloom and grow.
30. There is a lot of manure in the cow field.
31. You can look at a woolly caterpillar to forecast the winter.
32. The hurricane destroyed everything in its path.
33. Mr. Rolfe is a smart man.
34. You have to work hard to be successful.
35. Dad is the person that holds the family together.
36. She is always in pain.
37. The whole world is the setting in which people live out their lives.
38. Space is the one area in the world that hasn't been fully explored.
39. You can tell what someone is thinking and feeling by looking into her eyes.

Task L   pages 134-136
1. a
2. c
3. b
4. b
5. a
6. a
7. b
8. c
9. a
10. b
11. b
12. c
13. c
14. b
15. a
16. c
17. b
18. b
19. c
20. a
21. a
22. b
23. c

Task M   pages 137-138
1. I'm sure you didn't tell me.
   You told someone else.
   Someone else told me.
2. Others sit with us, but not her.
   She sits with other people.
   She sits with us, but not on the bus.
3. Am I going the right way?
   Is this how to get to the library or somewhere else?
   Am I going toward the library or away from it?
4. I can't believe you put salt in the tea.
   Are you the person who put salt in the tea?
   Did you put salt in the tea or in something else?
5. Nora came close to dropping my plate.
   Nora is the person who almost dropped my plate.
   Nora almost dropped my plate, not something else.
6. The book costs a little more or less than twelve dollars.
   The book costs about twelve dollars, not thirteen.
   The book, not the CD, costs about twelve dollars.
7. What is the reason he came home?
   Why didn't someone else come home?
   Why did he come home, rather than going somewhere else?
8. No, I said there aren't any spoons in the drawer.

There are forks in the drawer, but no spoons.

The spoons may be somewhere else besides in the drawer.

9. Fluffy is my cat's name, not my dog's.

Fluffy, not Stuffy, is my cat's name.

My cat's name is Fluffy, not yours.

10. The meeting is on Thursday, not another day.

Yes, I'm sure I told you the meeting was on Thursday.

I told you the meeting, not the lunch, was on Thursday.

11. The strawberries, not the peaches, are too ripe to eat.

Yes, I'm sure the strawberries are too ripe to eat.

The strawberries are too ripe, not too green, to eat.

12. Should there be something else tied to the mailbox?

Shouldn't the ribbon be tied to something else?

What is the reason for the ribbon on the mailbox?

13. Helen is never at school on Mondays.

Mondays are the days Helen misses school, not Tuesday.

Helen, not Krista, misses school every Monday.

14. You must pay for anything you drop.

You, not someone else, will have to pay for it.

It's okay to touch things, but if you drop something, you'll have to pay for it.

15. The Chipmunks, not the Tigers, are the best team!

The Chipmunks are indeed the best team!

The Chipmunks are the one and only best team!

16. Did I forget to tell you any part of the story?

Did I tell you or someone else the story?

Did I tell you the story, or did someone else tell you?

17. Karen, not Kara, left early.

Karen left early, not late.

Karen left early. She didn't arrive early.

18. Did Austin or someone else get on the school bus?

Did Austin actually get on the school bus?

Did Austin get on the school bus or the city bus?

19. Other people feed our dog, but not Lizzie.

Lizzie plays with our dog, but she doesn't feed him.

Lizzie feeds our cat, but not our dog.

20. The highest grade on the history exam, not the lowest, was 72!

The highest grade on the history exam, not the math exam, was 72!

The one and only highest grade on the history exam was 72!

Task N pages 139-141
Answers will vary.

Task O pages 142-144
2. Knots Out
3. Fun-cicles
4. Fine Shine
5. Quick Stick
6. Cuddle Time
7. Cool Fuel
8. Smoochie Poochies
9. Grime Grabber
10. Baby Bites
11. Toasty Toes
12. Shine 'n Sparkle
13. Power Out
14. Shade and Shield
15. Aqualicious
16. Garden Mist
17. Cloud Nine
18. Fast Fill
19. First Provident Bank
20. Purely Radiant
21. Fresh-a-licious
22. The Soothing Spa
23. Powerhouse
24. Glide and Ride
25. The High Steppers
26. What Zup?
27. Sprints
28. Eversharps
29. Lemon-Aid
30. Trap-Free

Task P pages 145-146
2. Something can't be both good and awful.
3. *Jumbo* means *large* and *shrimp* means *little*.
4. If it is *news*, it just happened. If it just happened, it isn't old.
5. Licorice is a black flavoring. If the candy is red, it can't be licorice.
6. We smile when we are happy, not sad.
7. A cushion is a soft pillow. If it is hard, it isn't a cushion.
8. *Nothing* and *much* are opposites. If we are doing much, we can't also be doing nothing.
9. A whisper is a very quiet way of speaking. If it is quiet, it can't also be loud.
10. A sip is a small amount, so if you take a big drink, it's not a sip.
11. *Pretty* and *ugly* are opposites. Something can't be pretty and ugly at the same time.
12. If we are in a mess, it can't be fine because *fine* means *good*.
13. *Half* means *one of two equal parts*; therefore, one part can't be larger.
14. *Advanced* means *skilled*; therefore, an advanced student is not a beginner.
15. Something new has just recently been made. If it didn't exist before, it can't be improved.
16. An alarm is a warning of danger. If no one can hear it, it won't alert anyone.
17. If you think, it is silent. If you say it aloud, you are talking.
18. A knot is tightly intertwined material. If it is tight, it can't also be loose.
19. *Favorite* means *the one you like the most*, not the least.

Answer Key, *continued*

20. If something is empty, it has nothing in it.
21. Glassware is made of glass; that's why it is called a *glass*.
22. If something is serious, it is not also fun.
23. If you are paid to work, you are an employee, not a volunteer.
24. If a show is taped, it is broadcast at a later date and can't be live.
25. History is the study of events that happened long ago. If it is modern, it happened now.
26. An estimate is a best guess. If a figure is accurate, it is exact.

Task Q   pages 147-148

1. no	9. yes
2. yes	10. no
3. yes	11. no
4. no	12. no
5. yes	13. yes
6. no	14. yes
7. no	15. yes
8. no	

Task R   pages 149-151

The client should say "Stop" after these sentences:

1. Of course she assigned us homework.
2. It's about three blocks down this street on the left.
3. No.
4. Of course I'll help you move on Saturday.
5. I finally decided to name him Fred.
6. Of course I'll scoot in.

7. It looks clear now, so I would go ahead and do it.
8. It goes in the garage on the workbench.
9. I ordered large drinks for the adults and small drinks for the children.
10. I heard on the radio that there's a big storm off the coast.
11. Look, the flag on the mailbox is down, so he must have come by already.

12. It's unlikely that coat will be on sale again within the next month.
13. The movie didn't get out until 9:45, and by the time we got out of the parking lot and drove home, it was 10:15.
14. No.
15. I think anything over $25,000 is way too much to spend on a car.
16. Her mother is my cousin.
17. The vet's name is Dr. McLean.
18. I probably left the front door open, and it must have wandered inside and into the dining room.
19. I didn't realize he would use it all.
20. The main difference between a hurricane and a typhoon is that hurricanes begin in the Atlantic Ocean and typhoons begin in the Pacific Ocean, particularly in the China Sea.
21. You won't be as likely to slip and fall, and they won't damage the boat.

19-10-987